CEREAL BOX

b · o · n · a · n · z · a

The 1950's

Identification & Values

Scott Bruce

COLLECTOR BOOKS

A Division of Schroeder Publishing Co., Inc.

The current values in this book should be used only as a guide. They are not intended to set prices, which vary from one section of the country to another. Auction prices as well as dealer prices vary greatly and are affected by condition and demand. Neither the Author nor the Publisher assumes responsiblility for any losses which might be incurred as a result of consulting this guide.

Searching For A Publisher?

We are always looking for knowledgeable people considered experts within their fields. If you feel that there is a real need for a book on your collectible subject and have a large comprehensive collection, contact us.

Layout design: Karen Geary
Cover design: Sherry Kraus

Dedication

For Beverly,
with my deepest gratitude and love.

Contents

Introduction

Think back to your childhood...those carefree days of show 'n tell, kickball, and braces. What kind of cereal did you eat? Lone Ranger Cheerios? Rice Honeys with the little plastic spoonmen? Pink Panther Flakes, which left that revolting liquid in the bottom of your bowl? Perhaps you craved Quisp or Freakies or Kellogg's OJ's? Or did your mother boycott the sugar-coated stuff in favor of...(gulp)...CREAM OF WHEAT?

No matter what you ate, you'll wish you'd had saved those weird packages and toy what-cha-ma-call-its from not-so-long ago. *The cereal box is back.* Once thought of as a sure sign of mental deficency like eating chalk or watching *Oprah,* collecting cardboard relics of breakfasts past is now an exploding hobby celebrated by *Newsweek, New York Times,* and *CBS Morning News.* Movie actor Mark Hamill collects cereal boxes. Cereal-loving Jerry Seinfeld told *USA Today* that he "subscribes to *Flake,*" the breakfast nostalgia magazine, and how he hopes that "somebody in the future will discover some Seinfeld Low-Fat Granola in some warehouse. That would be really exciting."

Why is cereal suddenly so cool? It's simple. The stressed-out nineties have discovered the breakfast table is the mother lode of our collective memories. Name one American who hasn't hit a home run on a belly full of Babe Ruth's Wheaties? Or didn't send a boxtop away to Sgt. Preston for a deed to a square inch of Klondike land? Or who didn't yell "I want my Maypo" until Mom reached for the rolling pin? Or go to school buzzed on Quisp "The Quazy energy cereal?" From All Bran to Breakfast with Barbie, Cocoa Krispies to Urkelos, Corn Flakes to Quangaroos, the cereal aisle is a true and accurate reflection of America's cultural psyche.

Dreaming...

over a bowl of Sugar Smacks, this little girl flashes her smile, just like *the* grain goddess Mary Hartline, in her mid-1950s kitchen.

Courtesy Allen C. Swan, Jr.

Cardboard Crazy

The product of an eight billion dollar home-grown industry, breakfast cereal is as American as jazz, muscle cars, or Hollywood movies. Yet unlike those pillars of American pop, cereal box collecting hasn't gotten the respect it deserves. The reason for this terrible oversight may be summed up in one word — *cardboard.* Whereas millions of packrats saved Louis Armstrong records, *Casablanca* lobby posters, and shiny '59 Corvettes, who, for crying out loud, saved old cereal boxes? Most souls see an empty cereal box and think trash. Mothers sacrificed stashes of Disneyland light ups or Twinkles boxes that escaped curb-side pick up to the hungry gods of spring cleaning. Up in smoke or buried in landfills are all the Trix, Stax, and Apple Jacks boxes we hollowed out each morning a bowlful at a time.

Or so it might seem to the uninitiated. In happy fact, vintage cereal boxes—made of the same durable stuff as baseball cards—are all over the place, once you learn where to look. Old stores, attics, pantry top shelves, warehouses, antique malls, and collectible shows are begging to share their crunchucopia with the savvy cereal hound. More and more sports collectors realize that cereal boxes are really big sports cards. Why settle for an itsy-bitsy Willie Mays card when you can have a *great big* Willie Mays Corn Flakes box? Once you take the plunge from the safety of your uncluttered world into the almighty cereal bowl, you'll be amazed at how fast your paperboard pets will colonize every corner of your hideaway.

In 1988, the cereal collecting bug climbed up my leg and sank its teeth into my left thigh. Overnight a delirium spread across my mind until I saw clear-as-day that the lurid, eye-popping graphics plastered across cereal boxes were *the greatest art the world has ever seen.* Leonardo, Van Gogh, Picasso, and other great artists were egg-sucking amateurs next to the quirky creators of Marky Maypo, Tony the Tiger, Trix Rabbit, and that grain god par excellance— Sonny the Cuckoo Bird...*Wuuuaaak! I'm Cuckoo For Cocoa Puffs...Cuckoo For Cocoa Puffs!*

To bring my flaky vision to the multitude, I got the crazy notion to map the entire breakfast table, decade by decade, from its humble turn-of-the-century beginnings to the present in a series of picture books. The project was insanely ambitious. A total innocent on the subject, I had no idea how deep and wide the bowl was I was wading into. My only model at the time was the lunch box collecting world, which turned out to be a stagnant frog pond next to cereal's vast Great Lakes. As find after find after find piled up in my basement, back hall, office, and shower stall, I began to feel like I was standing under Niagara Falls with my mouth open! Seven long...and gulping...years later, the book you hold in your hot little hands brings the first installment of that sugary vision into reality.

Modern Cereal Aisle is Born

The *Cereal Box Bonanza* series begins in the 1950's because that's when the cereal aisle as we know it today began. Presweetened cereals like Sugar Crisp, Frosted Flakes, and Cocoa Puffs were developed in the "Ike Era" as exciting alternatives to boring old Puffed Rice and oatmeal. To sell the new concoctions to kids, Disney-trained animators created cartoon pushers like Captain Jolly and Tony the Tiger who roared "They're *GR-R-R-REAT!*" in pitches televised right into our living rooms. Chanting war cries like "Sugar Pops are Tops!" and "Power up with Sugar Jets" boomers raced down to the supermarket to behold colorful, wide-eyed packages—the fruits of printing breakthroughs—and irresistible "Free Inside" bait until every one of us who had been on the planet less than 10 years was reduced to a whining, writhing, sticky-fingered knot of quibbering need. Sound familar?

Once at home, the appeal of cereal was more metaphysical than nutritional. When we sat down at the breakfast table with our favorite cereal hero, we entered into a kind of communion rite. Each spoonful of Lone Ranger Kix or Mary Hartline Sugar Smacks or Mr. Moonbird Jets lifted us out of the profane world of burnt toast, traffic reports, and unfinished home-work, and into the sacred world of our choosen grain god. To the skull-shaking beat of *crunch...crunch... crunch,* we became our hero—dreaming about daring rescues, paying off Dad's mortgage, and other feats until the last slurp of bowl-bottom nectar signaled it was time to wipe the mouth on the sleeve and push off to school.

Full of sparkling food for the eye, this book celebrates the grain gods that once reigned over our boomer childhoods from Olympuses of Corn Pops and Rice Krinkles. May it kick cereal boxes upstairs to their rightful place in the pop pantheon, while knock-ing boomers back to our bygone cereal days with gasps of "God, I remember that!"

What to Collect

So you want to collect cereal boxes for fun but don't know where to start? Easy. Go to your local supermarket. Flake makers spew out beautiful new box designs every quarter. Buy what you like, eat the cereal, and save the empty boxes. Boxes like the Boston Garden Commemorative Wheaties box are offered only in one region so you might pick up a few extras to trade with collectors in other parts of the solar system. In a year or two of active swapping,

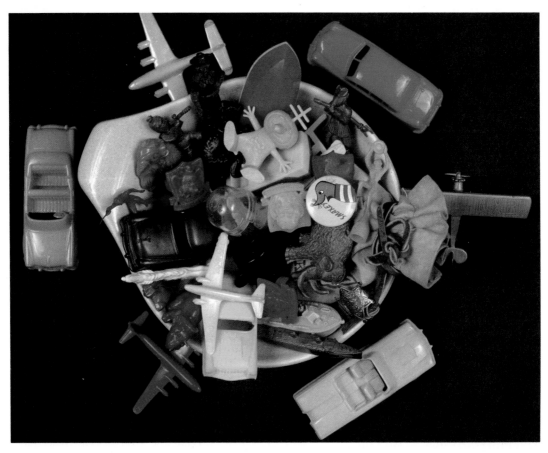

I remember that...
Cereal box trinkets or treasures — still in your dresser drawer at Mom's house or moved out during spring cleaning.

you'll be up to your eyeballs in hot flake containers (and probably presented with an ultimatum to chose between your collection or your spouse).

If you're collecting with an eye to resale, reach for the stars. In real estate, there's an old adage—"location, location, location." In cereal box collecting, it's "character, character, character." Characters are the famous movie, TV, or cartoon personalities—called Grain Gods—like Cap'n Crunch, Waldo, Tony the Tiger, and Michael Jordan, whom cereal makers splash across package fronts to catch our attention. "Cerealebrities" have charisma which rubs off on boxes as higher values. Even among recent offerings, the difference in price between a "Plain Jane" Wheaties box and one sweating with an athlete like Larry Bird or Joe Montana may be as much as $25.00 to $50.00.

How much you collect breakfast relics from the '50s, '60s, and '70s depends on your budget. Boxes sporting the Lone Ranger, Linus the Lionhearted, Quake, or the Beatles can command hundreds of dollars. If you don't wish to spend that much, collect the plainer, non-character boxes like Corn Flakes, Shredded Wheat, Toasties, or Cheerios. These boxes can be had for as little as $5.00 to $20.00. The type faces, colors, and swirling breakfast scenes reflect your childhood tablescape almost as well as their flashier star cousins—and at a fraction of the cost.

Like time-traveling robots, specialty collectors hunt down items with a common theme, regardless of the decade. Sports fans kill for Wheaties and other sports-related boxes featuring sluggers, tennis pros, and famous passers from the '30s to last year's Superbowl. Cartoon aficionados bounce to Bugs Bunny, Woody Woodpecker, and Roger Rabbit boxes. Vinyl-covered Dick Clark, Playboys, Monkees, and Archies boxes cling to rock 'n bowl lovers. Premium collectors drool over packages advertising hot prizes like the Gabby Hayes shooting cannon ring or Cap'n Crunch comic books. Still others horde Disney,

Western, space, or short-lived brands, or they may forsake boxes altogether in favor of magazine ads, plastic rings, commemorative dishes, or die-cut standees. The cereal universe is so enormous, its riches will satisfy nearly every collecting taste, however bizarre or pathetic. Dogs lovers, for example, have more than 50 cereal boxes to choose from including offers for trading cards, claw clippers, and a trusty pooper-scooper.

Where to Look

Though the prospect of collecting old cereal boxes might sound as ridiculous as mining on Mars, it's really as easy as picking up a newspaper. A classified ad in national collecting periodicals like *Antique Trader Weekly, Toy Shop,* and *Today's Collector* will generate a flood of responses. Before you advertise, figure out what you want to collect—Wyatt Earp Cheerios? Freakies toys? Space premiums? Maltex postcards? Everything Quisp and Quake? Colon-scrubbing muffin recipes from Kellogg's Good News? Then write your ad. Amid scores of offers for last month's Frosted Mini Wheats will be the occasional gem right up your alley. Often pickers stumble across caches of vintage Wheat Honeys or Sugaroos in old stores or warehouses and blow out their mega finds for peanuts through these widely-read publications. But you won't get lucky unless you advertise.

Through niche "zines" like *Flake: The Breakfast Nostalgia Magazine* and *The Freakies Magnet,* you'll be able to tap into a network of collectors around the globe from Boston to Zimbabwe. Buying, selling, and trading duplicates through these 'zines is a convenient way to bond with other breakfast buffs who share your affliction. *Flake* also runs display ads for reputable cereal dealers such as Quake, Just Kids Nostalgia, Tick-Tock Toys, and Hake's Americana, while not so reputable snakes-among-the-flakes are singled out for a massage from Grandpa's meat cleaver. Hailed by

Newsweek as a "real journalistic gem," *Flake* serves up fun for the whole family!

Collectibles shows are terrific places to have close encounters of the cereal kind, particularly if you wear a T-shirt or sign splashed with the slogan "FLAKE ME, BABY!" to alert passers by to your avocation/ personal problem. At the Atlantique City show in March every year, you might find a Mr. Fox hand puppet, a Pink Panther Flakes sample box, or a bunch of cereal newspaper ads to make the trip worthwhile. The annual Chicago Toy show is famous for Kellogg material, while the Indianapolis Advertising show is a reliable source for early die-cut cereal signs. Small flat items like decoder badges, plastic rings, and Mr. Waffles pocket comic books are usually found inside the glass-topped gem cases strewn across dealer tables. Often little loose items such as Cheerios air-planes, Captain Video spacemen, monster pop rockets, and King Vitaman hologram rings are harvested from the junk boxes dealers often stash under their tables. Great finds for a dollar or two may be bagged here—if you don't mind crawling on your hands and knees, and maybe having a Marlboro stubbed out on your hairpiece.

Caches of never-assembled cereal boxes called "flats" are popping up all over from industry sources such as printers, package designers, manufacturers, and their ad agencies. If you prefer a pristine package to an old one, collecting flats or package proofs may be your cup of tea. Once a flat is assembled into a box (bent and glued with rubber or neutral ph cement), it's worth about the same as an old cereal box that once fed a hungry family of four, particularily if the box is rare. Some collectors throw up their hands and never touch a box unless it actually held cereal once, while purists shudder at the sight of such damaged goods. (Let's pray that this bitter rift between boxheads and flat freaks doesn't tear at the hobby's intestines for too many years to come.)

Beginning collectors should be on the look out for laser reproductions passed off as the real McCoys. If a rare box you'd expect to sell for hundreds of dollars, such as a Yellow Submarine Wheat Honeys, is shrink wrapped and selling for a price that's too good to be true, it probably is.

Display and Storage

Since full cereal boxes are worth slightly more than empty ones, every beginning cereal box collector asks the same burning question—should I leave the cereal in the box or not? The answer depends on where, and how, you live. If pests are not a potential hazard, enclose the box in a clear plastic bag and forget about it. If you live in a broken-down house trailer and your full box of Berry Berry Kix runs the risk of being attacked by roaches, mice, rats, or Newt Gingrich, then, by all means, gut the box. This is done by gently pulling open the bottom tabs and removing the bag of cereal. (To test for bugs, put your ear to the box. If your hear strains of "Hi Ho, Hi Ho, off to work we go," it's occupied territory.)

Nothing is more heartbreaking than watching a swarm of weevils hatch out of your full Quake miner's helmet box come spring, so here's an easy alternative to gutting or fumigation (poisons are nasty…and who knows when you might get hungry?) Place the box in a clean plastic bag. Squeeze all the moisture-carrying extra air out of the bag and seal it with a twist tie and rubber band. Put the bag in your freezer for a few weeks. Don't hestitate to share this tech-nique with in-laws, nosey neighbors, or unwanted house guests. Their expressions as they watch the drama unfold between the frozen peas and the Häagen Dazs will be priceless.

Aside from attracting moths, small rodents, and large Republicans, unopened boxes tend to acquire a pear shape as the stuff inside settles and pushes out the sides. Take a tip from wine connoisseurs and rotate your boxes every few months to keep them in fighting trim.

Once you've built a collection, you'll probably want to display it somewhere. Cereal boxes may belong in the kitchen, but the adventurous collector may sprinkle them throughout the house or apartment in an effort to create a zany, retro-chic mood where WalMart meets Andy Warhol. (Warning: This may get out of hand. More than one non-collector spouse has declared "Cereal Box Free Zones" throughout the home.) While higgily-piggily clusters of boxes and prizes look okay together in a breakfast nook or dining room shrine, r-r-r-repetition is the key to a powerful cereal box display. A hundred or more boxes on a wall looks dynamite. Two hundred boxes on two walls looks nuclear. Four hundred boxes on four walls — the ultimate temple of the grain gods — will get Russian arms inspectors pounding on your front door. Don't be shy about expressing your innermost desire for iron-fisted control in cardboard — your friends and family already know you're nuts.

When displaying boxes, signs, or magazine ads in a room, remember that sunlight is their enemy. Ultraviolet radiation will rob a box of its brilliant color and value in months. To avoid fading, display your boxes on a wall or shelf away from direct sunlight, and change the items every few weeks. Besides, you'll probably want to keep the collection looking fresh by replacing stale Clackers with new Cruncheroos. If this is too much hassle, just paint your window-glass black, leaving a peephole here-and-there to watch for the UPS truck.

How you store your cereal box collection depends on your available space. If you can shoehorn the state of Rhode Island into your cellar, leave the boxes full in plastic bags or large storage boxes. If you live where space is in short supply, such as your car or pick-up truck, collapse the boxes by pulling open the flaps and gently flattening the box along the factory fold lines.

This way a huge collection may be safely broken down into a trunk-sized load, which still leaves plenty of room for your sleeping bag and Farrah Fawcett doll.

Like all paper collectibles, cereal memorabilia is best parked in a dry, cool environment. What's the point in going to all the trouble of scoring an old Lone Ranger Cheerios or Quisp raygun box, only to have it succumb to mildew? If your boxes begin to smell like old gym socks or the surface acquires mossy plaque like unbrushed teeth, move them to an air-conditioned room or buy a dehumidifier at once.

Where to Get More Information

Now that you've read this far, you'll probably want to check my facts against those of other, more sober-minded grain gurus. Fortunately for you, such references do exist. Here are the best sources for cereal skinny:

Books:

Cerealizing America: The Unsweetened Story of American Breakfast History by Scott Bruce and Bill Crawford. Published by Faber and Faber, Winchester, MA, 1995. $24.95. (An absolute *must* for any one interested in cereal.)

Tomart's Price Guide to Radio Premium and Cereal Box Collectibles by Tom Tumbusch. Published by Wallace-Homestead Book Company, Radnor PA. 1991. $22.95. (A cluttered reference that pictures in color many of the cereal boxes and premiums not included in *Cereal Box Bonanza: The 1950s*.)

Free Inside!: Breakfast Cereal Scale Model Car Identification by Larry Blodget. Published by Tech-Art Publications, PO Box 753, Rancho Mirage, CA 92270. $17.00. (Of interest to hardcore model car buffs only.)

Magazines:

Flake: The Breakfast Nostalgia Magazine, PO Box 481, Cambridge, MA 02140. Sample $5. Subscriptions are $18.95 for 5 issues. Free 25 word ad with subscription. (An indispensable collector clearing house and historical resource.)

Freakies Magnet: The Cereal Lover's Fanzine. Sample $4. Write: Kevin Meisner, 92B North Bedford Street, Arlington, VA 22201. (Covers breakfast offerings from the '60s to the present.)

Video Tapes:

Cereal Commercials, TV Lost & Found, PO Box 489, Schererville, IN 46375. $20 plus $3 shipping. (Barry McCann's anthology of old cereal ads is the best around.)

About the Prices in this Book

The prices in this book reflect the cereal memorabilia market in January, 1995, when the manuscript was completed. Values were arrived at more or less collectively with the informal help of other pundits including David Gutterman, Mitch Diamond, Larry Blodget, Steve Roden, Dan Goodsell, and Ken Farrell, who supplied cereal auction results.

Having said this, I must point out that the prices should be taken with a grain of salt…or sugar, as the case may be. Much can happen in the months between writing and publication, or the years between publication and revision, to impact on the market one way or the other. This is a guide, *not gospel.*

All prices are given for the item in the condition as pictured, whether an assembled flat or a half-crushed carton. I am not a condition wonk. Vintage cereal boxes are rare enough that only a fool would turn down a beautiful old box just because the flaps are torn off or a kid's name is scrawled across the face. Why deprive yourself of years of enjoyment by waiting for another box in better shape to come along? If you do, your precious unopened Banana Wackies box might be carried on the out stretched palm of the Grim Reaper.

Malcontents, constipated antique establishment types, and dealers looking to make a fast buck will grumble that I have shirked my solemn duty as an information purveyor by not delivering values for an inane range of possible conditions from "Just torched" to "Shoot, the ink is still wet!" Baloney! After wrestling a Mack truck of material up on my front lawn to make this book, even the thought of such nit-picking madness gives me a migraine. I leave that thankless job to some poor compulsive wretch who enjoys reading the Manhattan white pages or counting the half-moon marshmallow bits in a train load of Lucky Charms. Go fish.

What's in the Book

Though this book represents less than a tenth of the total cereal offers made between 1950 and 1959, rest assured it contains more than three-quarters of the most mouthwatering masterpieces of the decade. Under pressure from time and an empty-checking account, thousands of offers—some major, most minor—didn't make the cut. Jewels like the Howdy Doody inflatable, Captain Video flying saucer ring, Tom Corbett goggles, and a few Space Patrol Chex boxes may be mourned, but not zillions of boring come-ons for flatware, bird seed, and buttons.

What hurts are places in the book where I scored a great cereal box like the SAC survival rifle Toasties but couldn't bag the matching premium. AWOL prizes like the Roy Rogers jigsaw puzzles, Hickok deputy badges, and Jingles' plastic American rifles have marched beneath my nose at countless shows in the past seven years, but when I really needed to take their pictures—like the cops—they were nowhere to be found. Alas, I did locate some of these trinkets, but their owners, figuratively peering down the shotgun barrel while cats licked dirty dishes in the bathtub behind them, wouldn't consent to having them photographed for love or money. Collectors are a strange breed and *our* pecularities must be endured like a patch of bad weather or a touch of the flu. Let's hope that these unsightly rat holes will be plugged in the next edition of this book.

1950

In 1950...*North Korea invades South Korea...Cereal aisle tuned to radio shows like "Straight Arrow,"
"Roy Rogers," "Challenge of the Yukon," and "Hopalong Cassidy"...Sgt. Preston's Yukon Trail cutouts
give "mush" new meaning...Post confuses fans of Kellogg's "Mark Trail" radio show with "Mark a Trail
Hoppy's Way" promotion...Post imitates Ranger Joe with Sugar Crisp and a candy-coated krispie called
Krinkles...Pep's magno car ad shows a crystal ball and chirps "There's a Ford in your future!"...Snap,
Crackle, and Pop puppets pitch Rice Krispies on TV's "Singing Lady" and "Howdy Doody"...Injuns out of
Disney's "Hiawatha" go on warpath for Post Toasties...375,000 kids sip their morning juice from a
gaping hole in Roy Roger's plastic head!*

**Straight Arrow Injun-uity card –
Shredded Wheat**
National Biscuit Company, box back and spacer card, 6" tall and 7½" long.
1950–1952. $75.00 and $5.00.

Straight Arrow display – Shredded Wheat
National Biscuit Company, cardboard standee, 66" tall, 1949–1952.
$1,500.00. Photo by Peter S. Smith.

Roy Rogers souvenir cup

Quaker Oats Company, plastic, 4" tall, 1950. $25.00. Bob Hummrich Collection.

Roy Rogers souvenir cup poster

Quaker Oats Company, paper, 22" tall, 1950. $150.00.

Photo courtesy of Hake's Americana; York, PA.

Roy Rogers souvenir cup –
Quick Quaker Oats

Quaker Oats Company, tube side, 10" tall, 1950. $50.00.

Roy Rogers standee – Quaker Oats

Quaker Oats Company, cardboard, 6'2" tall, 1949–1950. $1,500.00. Don Phelps Collection.

Mother Knows Kellogg's Best display
Kellogg Company, jumbo display box with cardboard crown, 36" tall, 1950.
$145.00.

1950 Magno Ford car & instruction sheet – Pep
Kellogg Company. Car: plastic (ring missing), 3¼" long, 1950. $50.00.
Instructions: Paper, 10¾" tall, 1950. $15.00.

Snap, Crackle, and Pop hand puppets and newspaper ad

Kellogg Company, 1950. Puppets: cloth and vinyl, 8" tall, 1950. $25.00 – 40.00 each. Newsprint ad: 14" wide. $5.00.

"You'll love 'em together!" Corn Flakes and Raisin Bran newspaper ad

Kellogg Company, newsprint, 14" wide, 1950. $7.00.

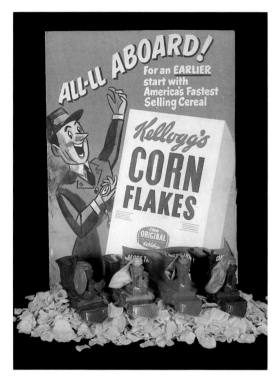

Jet drive whistle loco sales brochure – Corn Flakes (Cover and inside views)

Kellogg Company, paper, 14" tall, 1950. $50.00. Don Simonini Collection.

Jet-drive whistle locos

Kellogg Company, plastic, 5" long, 1950. $20.00–30.00 each. Don Simonini Collection.

Sgt. Preston Yukon Adventure cards – Puffed Rice
Quaker Oats Company, box front and back, 9" tall, 1950. $150.00.

Sgt. Preston Yukon Adventure cards
Quaker Oats Company, paper, 3½" tall, 1950. $10.00–15.00 each.

Sgt. Preston Yukon Trail – Puffed Rice

Quaker Oats Company, box front and back, 9" tall, 1950. $125.00.

Sgt. Preston Yukon Trail set

Quaker Oats Company, assembled cutouts, 24" wide, 1950. $100.00–150.00. John Fawcett Collection.

Sgt. Preston contest winner poster

Quaker Oats Company, paper, 22" tall, 1950. $150.00–200.00. Photo courtesy of Hake's Americana; York, PA.

Ranger Joe Wheat Honnies

Ranger Joe, Inc., empty cellophane bag, 11½" long, 1951. $150.00–200.00. Elliott H. Berger Collection.

Ranger Joe ranch mug

Ranger Joe Inc., white glass, 3" tall, early 1950s. $10.00.

Sugar Crisp magazine ad
Post/General Foods, paper, 14" tall, 1950. $4.00.

"Big News!" Post Tens magazine ad
Post/General Foods, paper, 14" tall, 1950–1952. $8.00.
Gary Hunter Collection.

Krinkles
Post/General Foods, sample box front, 4" tall, 1949–1950. $40.00.

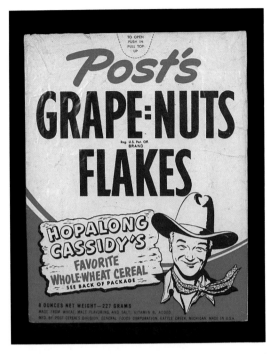 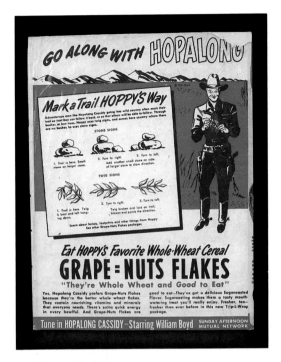

Hopalong Cassidy trail markings – Grape Nuts Flakes
Post/General Foods, box front and back, 8" tall, 1950. $200.00.

Hopalong Cassidy – Wheat Meal
Post/General Foods, sample box back, 4" tall, 1950.
$150.00. Mitch Diamond Collection.

Hopalong Cassidy banner
Post/General Foods, paper, approx. 30" long,
1950–1951. $300.00. Don Phelps Collection.

Hopalong Cassidy Wild West trading card –
Raisin Bran and Toasties

Post/General Foods, box fronts and back, 8" and 9½" tall, 1950–1951. $350.00 and $400.00.

Hopalong Cassidy Wild West trading cards

Post/General Foods, paper, 2½" tall, 1950–1951. $5.00–15.00 each. Cheryl Chambers Collection.

1951

In 1951...*Rosenbergs found guilty on espionage charges...Flake makers stampede onto TV with "Space Patrol," "Tom Corbett: Space Cadet," "Captain Video," and "The Roy Rogers Show"...Post adds yellow to its rotogravure printing, making Kellogg packages look bad...Inspired by Disney's "Treasure Island," a peg-legged pirate named Captain Jolly sails out on Post's Corn Fetti — the first sugar coated corn flake...Kellogg's Sugar Corn Pops goes stale in test market...Wiping milk from his beard, grizzled Gabby Hayes screeches "stand way back from your sets now" and fires a cannon load of Puffed Rice or Puffed Wheat right through the TV camera into the audience's bowls...Quaker commemorates the shtick with a miniature metal bombard called the "shooting cannon ring" — probably the largest cereal ring ever made!*

"8 Comic Books" ad

General Mills, comic book back cover, 7" wide, 1951. $15.00. Howard Bender Collection.

Disney comics – Wheaties

General Mills, box back, 8½" tall, 1950–1951. $200.00. John Fawcett Collection.

Disney pocket comics

General Mills, newsprint, 6" long, 1950–1951. $15.00–20.00 each. John Fawcett Collection.

Walt Disney fun masks
General Mills, assembled cutouts, 7–8½" tall, 1950–1951. $15.00–20.00 each.

Walt Disney fun mask – Wheaties
General Mills, box back, 10" tall, 1950–1951. $75.00–100.00.

"Masks on Wheaties Boxes!" ad
General Mills, comic book back cover, 7" wide, 1951. $15.00. Howard Bender Collection.

"Luscious" Corn Flakes display

Kellogg Company, jumbo box and cardboard, 65" wide, 1951. $450.00.

Tom Corbett: Space Cadet squadron – Corn Flakes

Kellogg Company, box back, 10" tall, 1951–1952. $200.00.

Please Touch Museum Collection.

Tom Corbett: Space Cadet squadron kit
Kellogg Company, assorted paper, cloth, and metal items, 1951–1952. $150.00–200.00. Please Touch Museum Collection.

Rocket rings
Kellogg Company, plastic, 1951. $20.00–30.00 each. Bob Hummrich Collection.

Rocket rings comic book ad (left)
Kellogg Company, newsprint, 7" wide, 1951. $10.00. Howard Bender Collection.

Flexing arm – Pep
Kellogg Company, back front, 10" tall. 1951. $25.00.

**"Howdy Doody's Favorite Treat"
Rice Krispies magazine ad**
Kellogg Company, paper, 14" tall. 1951. $5.00.

Rice Krispies
Kellogg Company, small display and regular box fronts, 10½" and 8" tall. 1951. $45.00 and $35.00.

Krinkles
Post/General Foods, box front and back, 7½" tall, 1951. $65.00.

Sugar Crisp magazine ad
Post/General Foods, paper, 14" tall, 1951. $5.00.

Hopalong Cassidy western badge – Raisin Bran
Post/General Foods, box front and back, 8" tall, 1950–1951. $400.00.

Hopalong Cassidy western badges
Post/General Foods, metal, 1" across, 1950–1951. $15.00–20.00 each. Virginia and Ralph Moody Collection.

"Heap Good Corn Flakes" newspaper ads – Toasties
Post/General Foods, newsprint proofs, 14" wide, 1951. $9.00 each.

Toy Indian canoes – Toasties
Post/General Foods, box front and back, 9¾" tall, 1951. $50.00.

Toy Indian canoes
Post/General Foods, waxed paper cutouts, 4½" long, 1951. $3.00 each.

Gabby Hayes prospector hat banner
Quaker Oats Company, paper, 21" wide, 1951. $250.00. Don Phelps Collection.

Gabby Hayes prospector hat
Quaker Oats Company, felt with braided chin strap, 12" across,
1951. $150.00. Don Phelps Collection.

Gabby Hayes comic book – Mothers Oats

Quaker Oats Company, oatmeal tube, 10", 1951, $75.00. Don Phelps Collection.

Gabby Hayes comic books

Quaker Oats Company, newsprint, 5" long, 1951. $20.00–35.00 each. Don Phelps Collection.

Gabby Hayes western gun collection – Puffed Wheat

Quaker Oats Company, box front and back, 9" tall, 1951. $200.00. John Fawcett Collection.

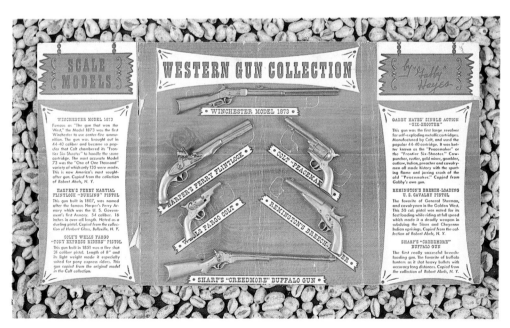

Gabby Hayes western gun collection

Quaker Oats Company, metal with cardboard display, 1½–4" long, 1951. $15.00–25.00 each. Jean Richmond Collection.

Gabby Hayes cannon ring – Puffed Rice
Quaker Oats Company, box front and back, 9" tall, 1951. $350.00.

Gabby Hayes cannon ring
Quaker Oats Company, various metals, 1½" long, 1951, $100.00–150.00.
Bob Hummrich Collection.

In 1952...USA explodes the first hydrogen bomb...Kellogg's new Life magazine packages blow away the competition with vivid color and star headshots designed to pop on color TV..."The Adventures of Wild Bill Hickok" loads "Bang—Bang, Sugar Pops are Tops" into the boomer lexicon...Katy Kangaroo and Tony the Tiger given equal billing on Sugar Frosted Flakes...Ike and Adlai mug it up on Corn Flakes...Ranger Joe trades in bags for boxes...Sgt. Preston still brays over radio waves...Li'l Abner's gang celebrates Sadie Hawkins Day (women asking men for dates) in Cream of Wheat magazine ads. "Daisy May was quite buxom," laughed Cream of Wheat president years later. "We found that when her blouse was cut a little lower, our readership went up!"

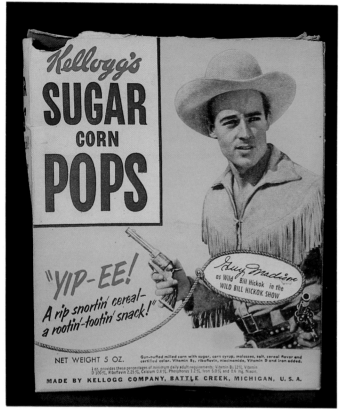 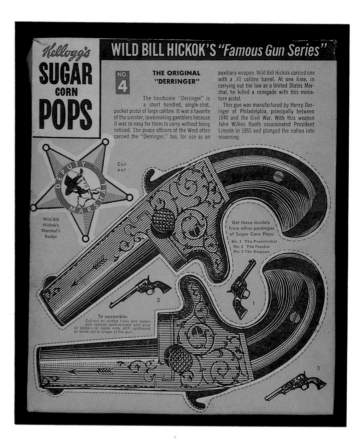

Wild Bill Hickok – Sugar Corn Pops
Kellogg Company, box front and back, 6" tall, 1952. $150.00.

Hickok Derringer and badge cutouts
Kellogg Company, paper, 6" across, 1952. $10.00.

Tom Corbett space goggles – Pep
Kellogg Company of Canada, box front and back, 8½" tall, 1952. $350.00.

Space scene – Pep
Kellogg Company of Canada, jumbo display box front, 20" tall, 1952. $250.00.

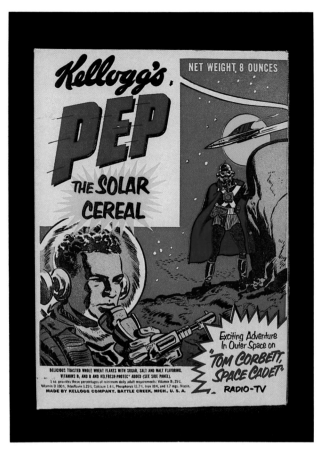

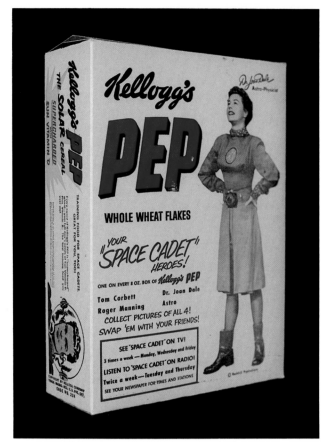

Tom Corbett: Space Cadet cast picture – Pep

Kellogg Company, box front and back, 8½" tall, 1952. $450.00.

Katy Kangaroo and Tony the Tiger – Sugar Frosted Flakes

Kellogg Company, sample boxes, 4" tall, 1952. $50.00.

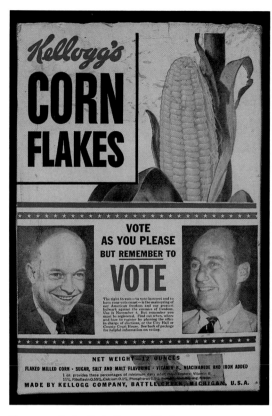

Ike and Adlai Corn Flakes
Kellogg Company, box front, 11½", 1952. $75.00.

"Sadie Hawkins Breakfast" magazine ad – Cream of Wheat
Cream of Wheat Company, paper, 14" tall, 1952. $8.00.

Sgt. Preston ore detector (map of Yukon blurb), coloring picture, and trail goggles – Puffed Rice
Quaker Oats Company, box fronts, 9" tall, 1952. $100.00–125.00 each.

Sgt. Preston ore detector and coloring picture – Puffed Rice
Quaker Oats Company, box backs, 9" tall, 1952. $125.00 and $100.00.

Sgt. Preston ore detector
Quaker Oats Company, plastic, 3" tall, 1952. $50.00. Ed Pragler Collection.

Sgt. Preston trail goggles – Puffed Rice
Quaker Oats Company, 1952. Left: Box back, 9" tall. $125.00. Above: Cutouts, 5½" across. $15.00.

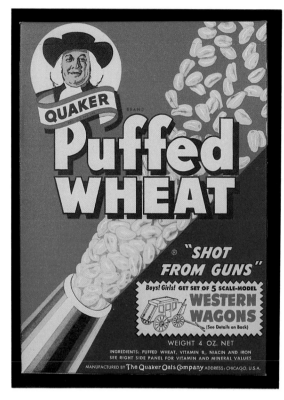

Gabby Hayes western wagons – Puffed Wheat

Quaker Oats Company, box front and back, 9" tall, 1952. $200.00.

Gabby Hayes western wagons

Quaker Oats Company, unassembled balsa and cardboard models, 5" across, 1952. $35.00 each. Jean Richmond Collection.

Ranger Joe Rice Honnies and Wheat Honnies

Ranger Joe, Inc, box fronts and back, 7½" tall, 1952–1954. $100.00 each.

Ranger Joe Honeyville airport

Ranger Joe, Inc, assembled cutout and plastic jets. Hanger 6" long and planes 1¾" long, 1952–1954. $10.00 each.

1953

In 1953...*Sen. Joseph McCarthy continues his anti-communist crusade..."Greatest Show on Earth" clowns Paul Jung and Lou Jacobs launch Kellogg's Ranger Joe clone — Sugar Smacks...Big G rings out "The Ding Dong School," and Smiles – "You can't help smiling the minute you taste it!"..."The Lone Ranger" is the most popular oater on TV...Roy and Dale slurp down "Delicious candy-kissed Krinkles," sing "Happy Trails to You," and beat out "Wild Bill Hickok" in the ratings game...Ralston's "Space Patrol" spews out a galaxy of "superific" space gadgets...Arthur Godfrey caresses Nabisco Shredded Wheat then defects to Kellogg's All Bran to the GR-R-REAT relief of seniors...Kellogg News proclaims the two-foot high Howdy Doody inflatable as "the perfect playmate!"*

Roy Rogers pop-out card – Toasties
Post/General Foods, box front and back, 11½" tall, 1952–1953. $300.00.

Roy Rogers pop-out cards
Post/General Foods, assembled paper, 3¼" tall, 1952–1953. $10.00–20.00 each. Roland Coover Collection.

Roy Rogers – Grape Nuts Flakes
Post/General Foods, box front, 10" tall, 1952–1953.
$150.00.

Roy Rogers pin backs –
Grape Nuts Flakes
Post/General Foods, metal, 1" across, 1953. $10.00–20.00.
Gary Hunter Collection.

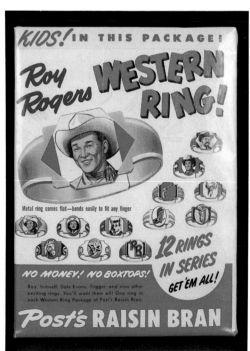

Roy Rogers western ring – Raisin Bran
Post/General Foods, box front and back, 8" tall, 1953. $350.00.

Roy Rogers western rings
Post/General Foods, metal, 3" long, 1953. $10.00–15.00 each.
Virginia and Ralph Moody Collection.

Roy Rogers western medal and Captain Video space man – Raisin Bran
Post/General Foods, box fronts, 8" tall, 1953. $200.00 and $350.00.

Roy Rogers western medal and Captain Video space man – Raisin Bran
Post/General Foods, box backs, 8" tall, 1953.

Roy Rogers western medals
Post/General Foods, metal, 1½–2" across, 1953. $15.00–20.00 each. Gary Hunter Collection.

Captain Video space men
Post/General Foods, plastic, 1½" tall, 1953. $10.00–15.00 each.

"New" Corn Fetti magazine ad
Post/General Foods, paper, 14" tall, 1953. $5.00.

Captain Jolly Corn Fetti
Post/General Foods, box front, 9½" tall, 1953. $75.00.

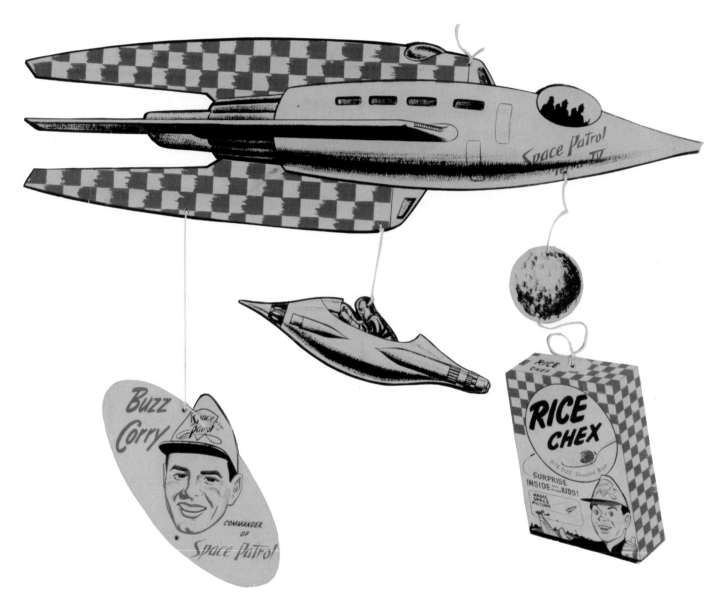

Space Patrol Rice Chex mobile
Ralston Purina, die-cut cardboard, 27" across, 1953. $500.00—750.00. Photo courtesy Hake's Americana, York, PA.

Space Patrol magic space picture and space binoculars – Rice Chex
Ralston Purina, box front, 9" tall, 1953. $350.00.

Space Patrol magic space picture and space binoculars – Wheat Chex
Ralston Purina, box front and back, 9" tall, 1953. $350.00.

Space Patrol binoculars and mystery pictures
Ralston Purina, 1953. Binoculars: plastic, 5". $150.00. Mystery pictures: paper, 4" tall. $10.00 each. Roland Coover Collection.

Space Patrol hydrogen ray gun ring
Ralston Purina, metal and plastic, 1½" long, 1954. $150.00–200.00.

Bob Hummrich Collection.

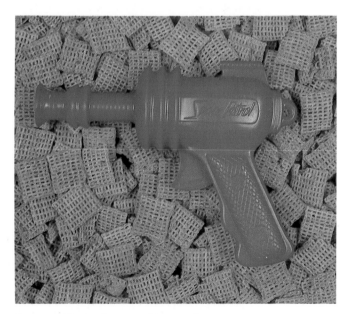

Space Patrol cosmic smoke gun
Ralston Purina, plastic, 4½" long, 1952–1955. $75.00–125.00.

Don Simonini Collection.

Space Patrol outer space helmet
Ralston Purina, die-cut paper, 14" tall. 1953–1955. $100.00–150.00.
Ed Pragler Collection.

**Space Patrol
man from Mars totem head**
Ralston Purina, die-cut paper, 15" tall, 1954. $50.00.

Space Patrol project-o-scope
Ralston Purina, Chex box side panels and plastic toy. Rocket
6¼" tall, 1953. $250.00. Ed Pragler Collection.

48 state and foreign license plates – Wheaties

General Mills, box fronts, 10" tall, 1953. $50.00 each.

48 state and foreign license plates – Wheaties

General Mills, box backs, 10" tall, 1953. $50.00 each.

Miniature 48 state license plates

General Mills, stamped metal, 4–5" wide, 1953. $5.00–15.00 each. Don Simonini Collection.

Miniature foreign license plates
General Mills, stamped metal, 4–5" wide, 1953. $5.00–15.00 each.
Don Simonini Collection.

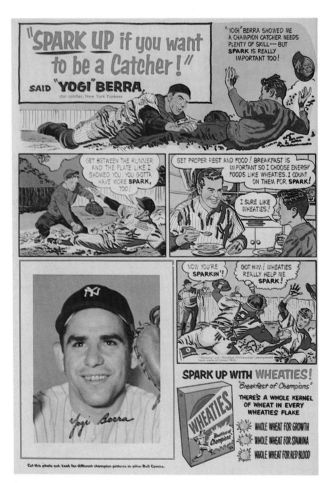

Yogi Berra Wheaties ad
General Mills, comic book back cover, 7" wide, 1953. $15.00.

Howard Bender Collection.

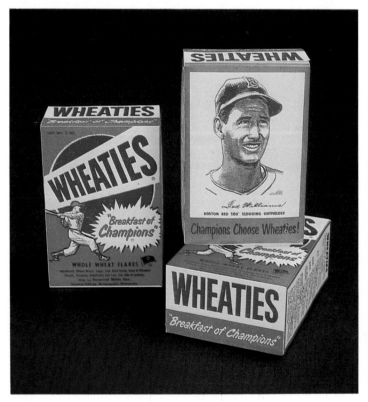

Ted Williams portrait – Wheaties
General Mills, single-serving boxes, 4" tall, 1953. $250.00.

John Fawcett Collection.

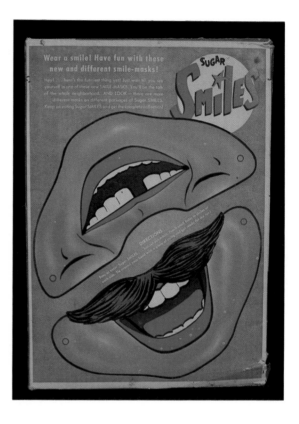

Sugar Smiles

General Mills, box front and back, 9½" tall, 1953. $100.00.

Cheerios and Ding Dong School Kix

General Mills, box fronts and Kix back, 10¼" tall, 1953. $25.00 and $50.00.

Arthur Godfrey coupons – Shredded Wheat

National Biscuit, box back and cardboard shelf talker, 6" tall and 16" wide, 1953. $80.00 and $50.00.

"Choo…choo…choose your favorite"
Variety Pack magazine ad

Kellogg Company, paper, 14" tall, 1953. $5.00.

Sweetheart of the Corn – Corn Flakes

Kellogg Company, display box front, 10¼" tall, 1953. $45.00.

Rice Krispies

Kellogg Company, display and Howdy Doody inflatable box fronts, 10¼" and 8" tall, 1953. $50.00 and $300.00.

Inflatable Howdy Doody doll – Rice Krispies

Kellogg Company, box back, 8" tall, 1953. $300.00.

**Inflatable Tony the Tiger doll –
Sugar Frosted Flakes**
Kellogg Company, box back panel, 9½" tall, 1953. $15.00.

Inflatable Tony the Tiger doll
Kellogg Company, vinyl, 45" tall, 1954. (Second, taller offer.)
$250.00–300.00. Phil Arthurhultz Collection.

"GR-R-REAT!" Tony the Tiger Sugar Frosted Flakes newspaper ad

Kellogg Company, newsprint proof, 14" across, 1953. $15.00.

"A dish you shouldn't miss" Felix Adler Sugar Smacks newspaper ad

Kellogg Company, newsprint proof, 14" wide, 1953. $25.00.

Paul Jung Sugar Smacks
Kellogg Company, box front, 9½" tall, 1953. $300.00.

Lou Jacobs Sugar Smacks
Kellogg Company, box front, 9½" tall, 1953. $200.00.

Paul Jung and Lou Jacobs shuttle-action toy
Kellogg Company, die-cut cardboard, 10" long, 1953. $45.00.
Please Touch Museum Collection.

Jingles – Sugar Corn Pops
Kellogg Company, box front, 7¼" tall, 1953. $125.00.

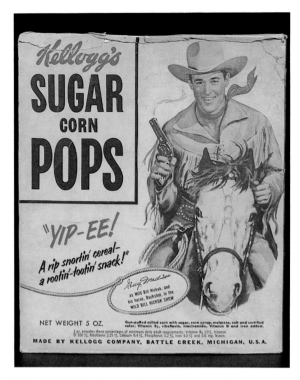

Wild Bill Hickok – Sugar Corn Pops
Kellogg Company, box front, 7¼" tall, 1953. $125.00.

Wild Bill Hickok – Sugar Corn Pops
Kellogg Company, jumbo display box front, 20" tall, 1953. $150.00.

1954

In 1954...USA launches first atomic-powered sub, Nautilus...Big G rolls out Trix and Sugar Jets in boxes that glow like the sub's reactor core...Captain Midnight keeps the world free for Kix, while Major Jet urges kids to "Feel jet powered with Jets"...Nabisco buys Ranger Joe, changes Honnies to Honeys and boots off Joe for Buffalo Bee, a six-gun toting insect voiced by Mae "Betty Boop" Questel...Nabisco's "Adventures of Rin Tin Tin" becomes huge TV hit...Norman Rockwell serves Americans freckled kids for breakfast on Corn Flakes...Kellogg trashes "Tom Corbett: Space Cadet" for "The Adventures of Superman"...Tony gives Katy the Kangaroo the heave-ho...A Kellogg man admits that their whole-wheat flake Pep "was getting its lunch eaten by Wheaties."

Lone Ranger comic books – Cheerios

General Mills, 1954. Box front: 9½" tall. $300.00. Comics: newsprint, 5" long. $25.00–50.00 each. Don Phelps Collection.

Lone Ranger Moon Flower mask – Wheaties

General Mills, box front and back, 8½" tall, 1954. $150.00.

Lone Ranger masks
General Mills, cutouts, 8–9" tall, 1954. $15.00–25.00 each. Steve Roden Collection.

Phonograph records – Wheaties
General Mills, box front and back, 10" tall, 1954. $75.00.

Trix

General Mills, sample boxes, 4¼" tall, 1954. $45.00 each.

"Pour a rainbow for breakfast tomorrow" Trix magazine ad

General Mills, paper, 14" tall, 1954. $7.00.

Major Jet film-o-vision and sample Sugar Jets

General Mills, box fronts and back, 4¼" and 8" tall, 1954. $100.00 and $45.00.

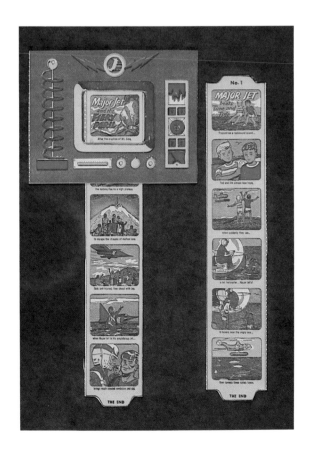

Major Jet magic paint set book #2

General Mills, paper, approx. 7" wide, probably 1954. $15.00.

Major Jet film-o-vision

General Mills, cardboard cutout, 8¼" long, 1954. $10.00.

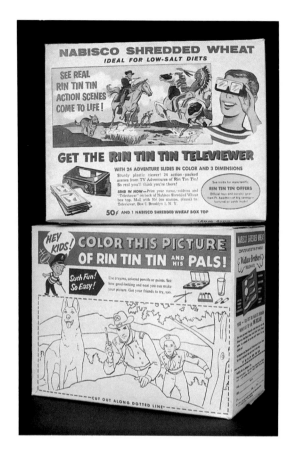

Rin Tin Tin Televiewer and "Color this picture" – Shredded Wheat

National Biscuit Company, box backs, each 6" tall, 1954. $150.00 and $85.00.

Rin Tin Tin televiewer and cards

National Biscuit Company, plastic and cardboard, 4" across, 1954. Set $75.00. Ed Pragler Collection.

Roy Rogers paint set – Sugar Crisp
Post/General Foods, box front and back, 9½" tall, 1954. $200.00.

"For golden honey flavor"
Sugar Crisp magazine ad
Post/General Foods, paper, 11" tall, 1954. $7.00.

Railroad emblems Sugar Crisp newspaper ad
Post/General Foods, paper proof, 14" wide, 1954. $15.00.

Sugar Crisp railroad emblems (above)
Post/General Foods, stamped metal, 4" across, 1954. $15.00–25.00 each. Don Simonini Collection.

Sugar Crisp railroad fun book (right)
Post/General Foods, newsprint, 10" tall, 1954. $15.00–25.00. Don Simonini Collection.

Captain Jolly comic book – Corn Fetti
Post/General Foods, box front and back, 9½" tall,1954. $150.00.

Captain Jolly comic books
Post/General Foods, newsprint, 5" across, 1954. $25.00–35.00 each. Steve Roden Collection.

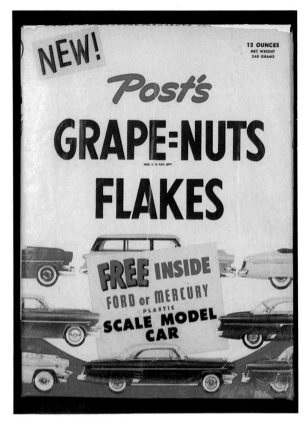 

Ford or Mercury scale models – Grape Nuts Flakes
Post/General Foods, box front and back, 10" tall, 1954. $200.00.

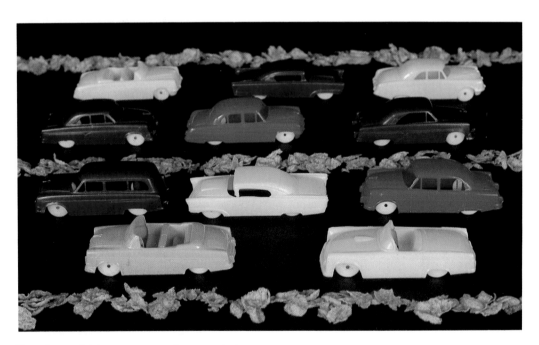

Ford and Mercury scale models
Post/General Foods, plastic, 3" long, 1954. $20.00–50.00 each. Larry Blodget Collection.

Superman stereo-pix – Sugar Frosted Flakes

Kellogg Company, box fronts, 9½" tall, 1954. $300.00 each.

"I'd stalk a mile for…" Sugar Frosted Flakes magazine ad

Kellogg Company, paper, 14" tall, 1954. $7.00.

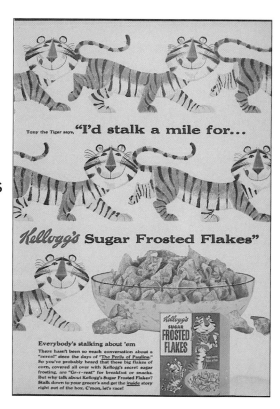

Superman stereo-pix – Sugar Frosted Flakes

Kellogg Company, box backs, 9½" tall, 1954. $300.00 each.

Superman stereo-pix

Kellogg Company, assembled cutouts, 8" wide, 1954. $10.00–15.00 each.

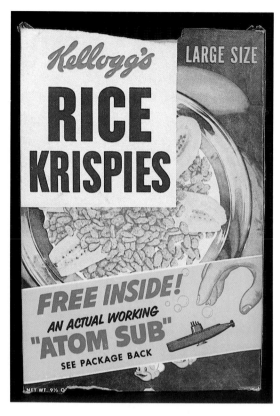

Atom sub – Rice Krispies
Kellogg Company, box front and back, 10¼" tall, 1954–1955. $125.00.

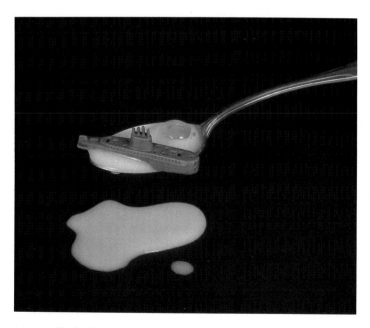

Atom Sub toy
Kellogg Company, plastic, 2¼" long, 1954–1955. $15.00.

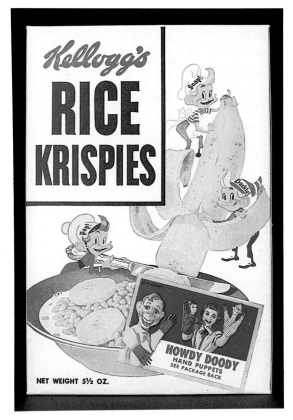

Howdy Doody hand puppets – Rice Krispies
Kellogg Company, box front and back, 9½" tall, 1954. $250.00.

Howdy Doody hand puppets
Kellogg Company, vinyl and cloth, 7" tall, 1954. $50.00–75.00 each. Jeff Judson Collection.

Howdy Doody mask – Rice Krispies
Kellogg Company, box front and back, 10¼" tall, 1954. $300.00. Don Phelps Collection.

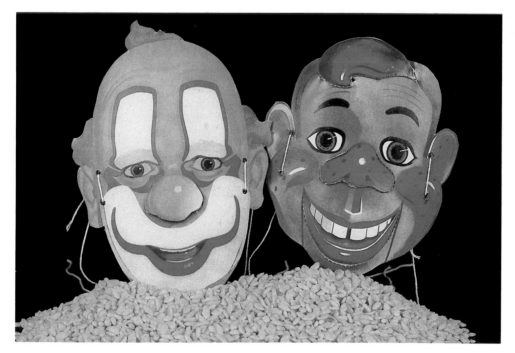

Howdy Doody and Clarabell masks
Kellogg Company, assembled cutouts, 9" tall, 1954. $15.00–25.00 each. Jeff Judson Collection.

U.S. Navy frogmen sign – Corn Flakes

Kellogg Company, diecut cardboard on a stick, 14" tall, 1954. $500.00.

U.S. Navy frogmen – Corn Flakes

Kellogg Company, box back panel and plastic figures, 1954. Box: 11½" tall. Frogmen figures: 2" tall, $15.00–25.00 each. John Fawcett Collection.

In 1955...USA sends advisors to train South Vietnamese army...Ted Williams bats baseball team patches from Sugar Crisp...Post unleashes a cartoon baker on 40% Bran Flakes..."Sgt. Preston of the Yukon" sleds to TV and his deed to one-square inch of the Klondike triggers a major land grab among children...Hugh O'Brian tells kids to "Eat Gleem and Brush with Cheerios" in commercials during "The Life and Times of Wyatt Earp"...Mary Hartline shows skin on the back of Frosted Flakes...Kellogg drops plastic dogs into Rice Krispies boxes to promote "The Lady and the Tramp." "Disney was murder," recalled a Kellogg man, who said NO to Walt having his name bigger than W.K.'s "It was vulgar...you had a feeling you were trying to sort something out in a school yard."

Rockwell kid – Corn Flakes

Kellogg Company, jumbo display box front, 20" tall,
1955–1956. $125.00.

Fighter plane – Corn Flakes

Kellogg Company, box front, 11½" tall, 1954–1955.
$100.00.

Dingle dangle – Corn Flakes

Kellogg Company, box front and back, 9½" tall, 1955. $100.00.

Tony the Tiger and Clarabell dingle dangles
Kellogg Company, cardboard cutouts, 5¾" across, 1955. $15.00–20.00 each. Jeff Judson Collection.

Flying Superman – Corn Flakes
Kellogg Company, box fronts, 9½" tall, 1955. $350.00.

Flying Superman – Corn Flakes
Kellogg Company, box back, 9½" tall, 1955. $350.00.

Flying Superman
Kellogg Company, plastic, 6½" wide, 1955. $100.00–150.00.

Superman rocket and Dragnet whistle – Corn Flakes
Kellogg Company, box fronts, 9½" tall, 1955. $250.00 and $100.00.

Superman rocket and Dragnet whistle – Corn Flakes

Kellogg Company, box backs, 9½" tall, 1955. $250.00 and $100.00.

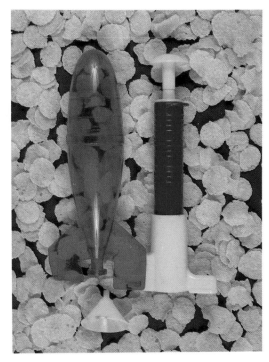 

Superman rocket

Kellogg Company, plastic, 6" tall, 1955. $75.00–150.00.

Ed Pragler Collection.

Dragnet whistle

Kellogg Company, plastic, 2" long, 1955. $10.00–15.00.

Superman belt – Corn Flakes
Kellogg Company, box front and back, 9½", 1955–1956. $250.00.

Superman belt
Kellogg Company, vinyl and metal. Buckle: 2¾" wide, 1955–1956. $200.00–250.00.

Major Jet's rocket glider – Sugar Jets
General Mills, box front and back, 8½" tall, 1955. $150.00.

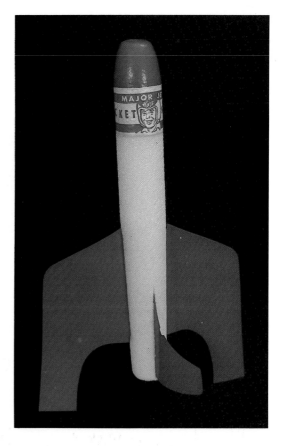

Major Jet's rocket glider (right)
General Mills, styrofoam and plastic, 10" tall, 1955. $150.00. Steve Roden Collection.

Major Jet's rocket glider/Sugar Jets newspaper ad (below)
General Mills, newsprint, 14" across, 1955. $7.00.

Tonto belt – Trix

General Mills, box front and back, 8½" tall, 1955. $350.00 each.

Tonto belt

General Mills, leather and beads, 25" long, 1955. $35.00.
Lee Felbinger Collection.

Lone Ranger branding iron – Kix

General Mills, box front and back, 10" tall, 1955. $250.00.

Wyatt Earp Paterson and Peacemaker pistol – Cheerios

General Mills, box fronts, 8½–10¼" tall, 1955. $125.00 each.

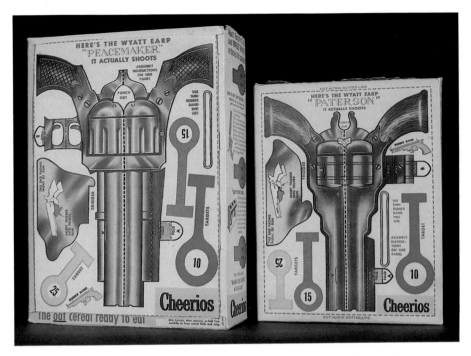

Wyatt Earp Paterson and Peacemaker pistol – Cheerios
General Mills, box backs, 8½–10¼" tall, 1955. $125.00 each.

Wyatt Earp Paterson and Peacemaker pistol target game
General Mills, assembled cardboard cutouts, 7–8" long, 1955. $20.00–35.00.

Rin Tin Tin ring – Rice Honeys
National Biscuit Company, box front and back, 7½" tall, 1955. $100.00.

Rin Tin Tin rings
National Biscuit Company, plastic, ¾" across each, 1955. $10.00–15.00 each. Roland Coover and Bob Hummrich Collections.

Sgt. Preston Klondike deed – Puffed Wheat
Quaker Oats Company, box front and back, 9" tall, 1955. $150.00.

Sgt. Preston Klondike deeds
Quaker Oats Company, paper, 8" across, 1955. $15.00. Steve Roden and Dan Woods Collections.

Sgt. Preston Klondike prospector's pouch
Quaker Oats Company, Yukon deed box side panel, chamois cloth, 4½" tall, 1955. $45.00. Ed Pragler Collection.

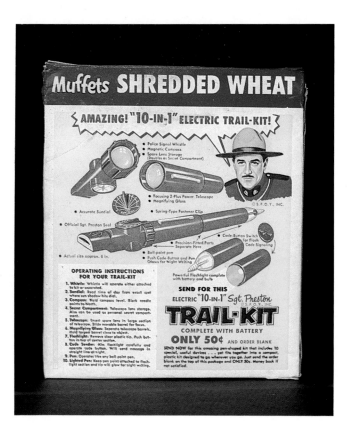

Sgt. Preston 10-in-1 trail kit – Muffets

Quaker Oats Company, box front and back, approx. 8" tall, 1956. $125.00. John Fawcett Collection.

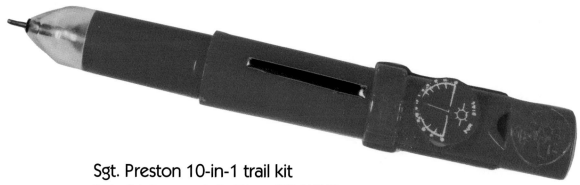

Sgt. Preston 10-in-1 trail kit

Quaker Oats Company, plastic, 6" long, 1956. $125.00. Photo courtesy of Hake's Americana, York, PA.

 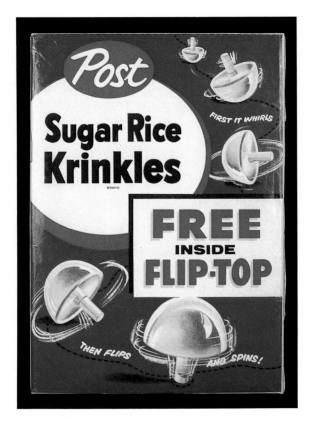

Flip-top Sugar Rice Krinkles
Post/General Foods, box front and back, 9" tall, 1955. $45.00.

Captain Jolly Sugar Corn Fetti
Post/General Foods, box front, 9" tall, 1955. $125.00.

Roy Rogers golden records and Ted Williams patches – Sugar Crisp
Post/General Foods, box fronts and backs, 9½" tall, 1955. $200.00 and $350.00.

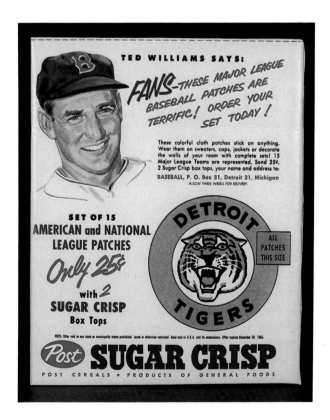

Roy Rogers golden records
Post/General Foods, plastic, 6" across, 1955. $15.00–25.00 each. Peter Muldavin Collection.

Original Roy Rogers artwork for golden records Sugar Crisp box
Tempera on illustration board by Robert Traverse. Image 9½" long, 1955. $50.00–75.00.

Betty Ann Bunger Collection.

"Flavor inning" Sugar Crisp magazine ad
Post/General Foods, paper, 14" tall, 1954–1955. $5.00.

Blackstone magic trick and Fruehauf tractor trailer – Sugar Crisp
Post/General Foods, box fronts and backs, 9½" and 8" tall, 1955. $125.00 each.

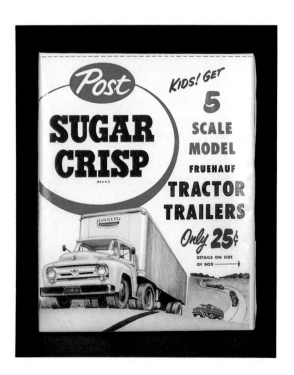

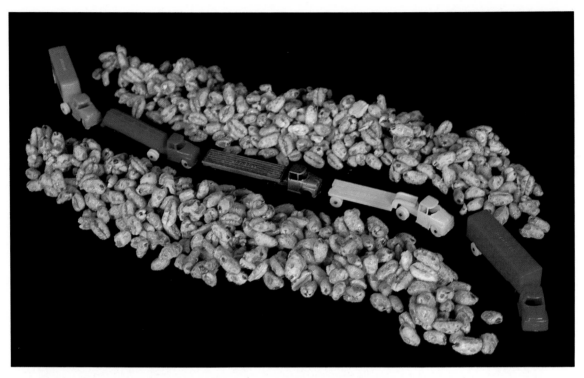

Fruehauf tractor trailers
Post/General Foods, plastic, 3" long, 1955. $15.00 each. Larry Blodget Collection.

"Gobblin' food"
Sugar Crisp magazine ad
Post/General Foods, paper, 14" tall, 1955. $5.00.

Scale model Ford – Grape Nuts Flakes
Post/General Foods, box front and back, 10" tall, 1955. $175.00.

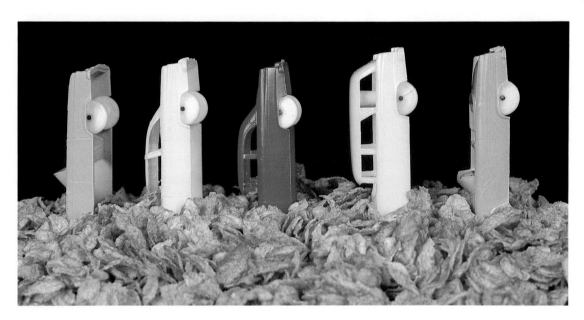

Scale model Fords
Post/General Foods, plastic, 3" long, 1955. $15.00–25.00. each.

Kannon Ball freight train and regular 40% Bran Flakes

Post/General Foods, box fronts and back, 10½" and 8½" tall, 1955. $100.00 and $25.00.

Kannon Ball freight train

Post/General Foods, plastic set in cardboard box. Cars: 8–12" long, 1955. $75.00.
Don Simonini Collection.

"Win your own pony" Toasties magazine ad
Post/General Foods, paper, 14" tall, 1955. $9.00.

Roy Rogers – Grape Nuts Flakes and Century boat – Grape Nuts
Post/General Foods, box fronts, 9" and 6½" tall, 1955. $100.00 each.

Roy Rogers – Grape Nuts Flakes and Century boat – Grape Nuts
Post/General Foods, box backs, 9" and 6½" tall, 1955. $100.00 each.

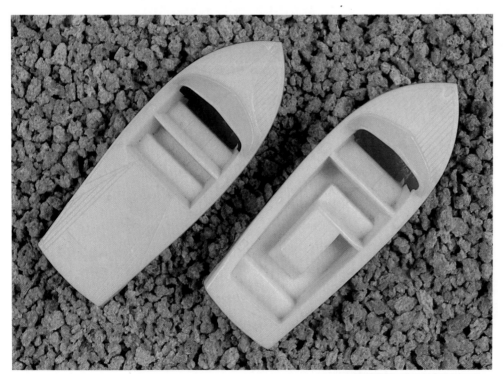

Century boats
Post/General Foods, plastic, 3" long, 1955.
$15.00 each.

PT boat and printing set – Rice Krispies
Kellogg Company of Canada, box fronts and back, 8" tall, 1955. $75.00 and $25.00.

PT boat
Kellogg Company of Canada, plastic, 2" long, 1955. $15.00.

Lady & Tramp statuette, toy train, and famous jets of the world – Rice Krispies
Kellogg Company (United States and Canada), box fronts and backs, 8" tall, 1955. $125.00, $25.00, and $50.00.

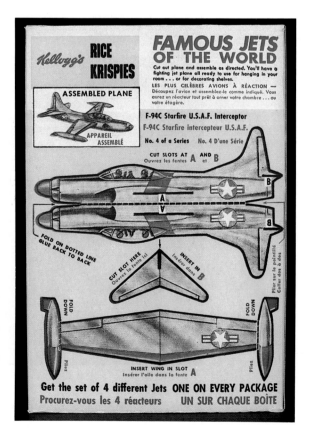

Lady & Tramp statuettes

Kellogg Company, plastic, 2" tall, 1955. $15.00–25.00 each. Graham Trievel Collection.

F-94C Starfighter

Kellogg Company of Canada, assembled cutout, 5½" long, 1955. $10.00.

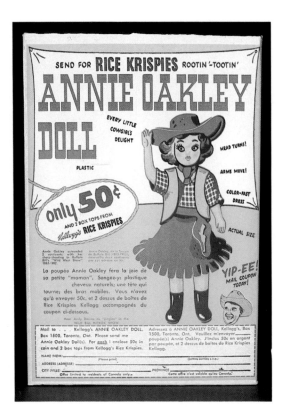

Annie Oakley doll – Rice Krispies

Kellogg Company of Canada, box front and back, 10¼" tall, 1955. $100.00.

Annie Oakley doll

Kellogg Company of Canada, plastic, vinyl and cloth, 8¼" tall, 1955. $25.00.

U.S. Navy Frogmen (Jingles) – Sugar Pops
Kellogg Company, box front and back, 7½" tall, 1955. $150.00.

Old time gun (Hickok) – Sugar Pops
Kellogg Company, box front and back, 7¼" tall, 1955. $125.00.

U.S. Navy frogmen – Corn Flakes
Kellogg Company, plastic, 3½" tall, 1955. $15.00–25.00 each.

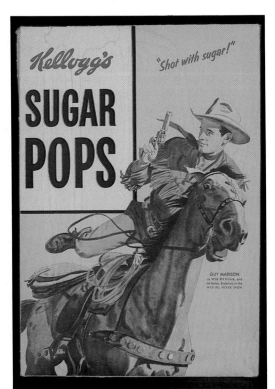

Wild Bill Hickok – Sugar Pops
Kellogg Company, jumbo display box front, 20" tall, 1955.
$125.00.

Mary Hartline magic doll – Sugar Frosted Flakes

Kellogg Company, box front and back, 9½" tall, 1955. $225.00.

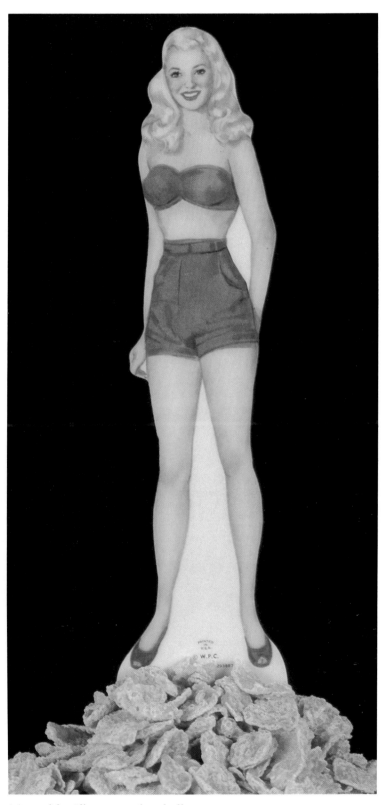

Mary Hartline magic doll

Kellogg Company, plastic film over cardboard, 9½" tall, 1955. $45.00.

Jim Cole Collection.

Mary Hartline – Sugar Smacks
Kellogg Company, jumbo advertising display box
[faded], 20" tall, 1955. $100.00–200.00.

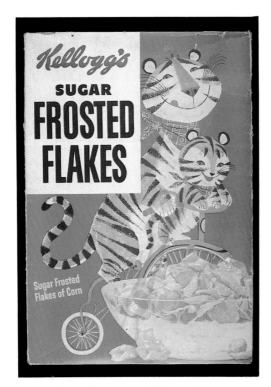

Tony the Tiger and Tony Jr. –
Sugar Frosted Flakes
Kellogg Company, jumbo display box front, 20" tall,
1955. $150.00.

"You bet your life"
Frosted Flakes magazine ad
Kellogg Company, paper, 14" tall, 1955. $10.00.

1956

In 1956...*Interstate highway system inaugurated...Post's white packages pick up the corner balloon and other Kellogg ideas...Captain Jolly climbs rigging to slash away at Tony the Tiger before sinking beneath the waves...Big G rolls out Cocoa Puffs...Wheaties introduces "The Face" package during motivational research craze. Blue "mother," yellow "sister," red "brother," and brown "father" lure family members according to their primal color needs...Boxes of Trix, Wheaties, Cheerios, Jets, and Kix run Disneyland scenes called "light ups" to sell the struggling theme park to the public...A pint-sized buckaroo named Marky screams "I want My Maypo!" and steals the show. "This is the first time a TV commerical has bred a character that became the logotype in product packaging," crows a Maypo ad man.*

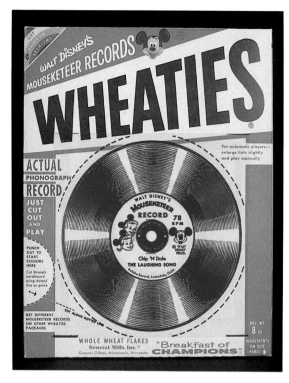

Mouseketeers record – Wheaties

General Mills, box front and back, 8½" tall, 1956. $100.00.

Onpack Mouseketeers records

General Mills, cutout records, 6" across, 1956. $10.00–15.00 each. Steve Miller Collection.

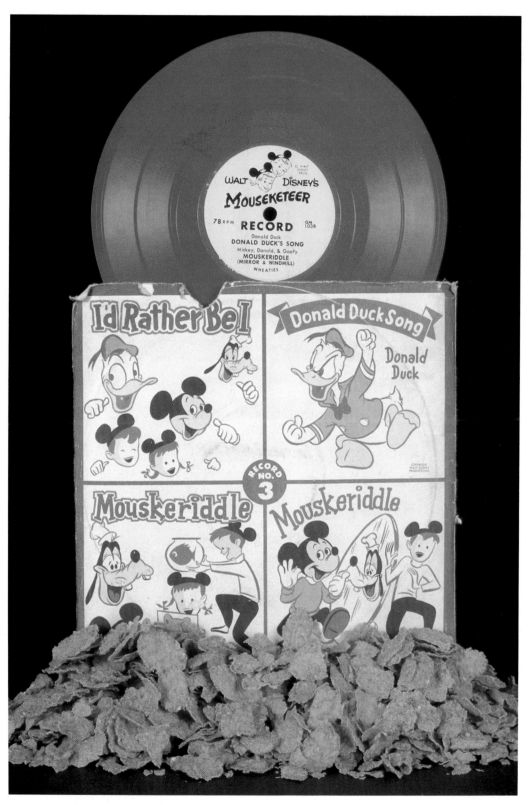

Mouseketeer record
General Mills, orange plastic, 7" across, 1956. $45.00.

Mickey Mouse ring – Sugar Jets

General Mills, box front and back, 8½" tall, 1956. $300.00. Please Touch Museum Collection.

Mickey Mouse and his pals rings

General Mills, plastic, 1" tall, 1956. $25.00–45.00 each.

Disneyland Park light-ups newspaper ad
General Mills, newsprint, 10½" across, 1956. $5.00.

Disneyland light-ups – Kix and Trix
General Mills, box fronts, 8½" to 10" tall, 1955–1956. $100.00–200.00.

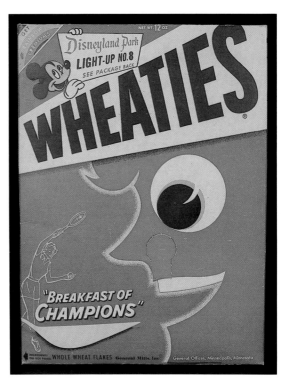

Disneyland light-ups – Sugar Jets and Wheaties
General Mills, box fronts, 8½" to 10" tall, 1955–1956. $100.00–200.00.

Face – Wheaties
General Mills, box fronts, 10" tall, 1956. $100.00–200.00.

Disneyland light-ups

General Mills, various box backs, 8½" tall, 1955–1956.
$100.00–200.00.

Disneyland light-ups

General Mills, various box backs, 10" tall, 1955–1956.
$100.00–200.00.

Blackboard – Wheaties
General Mills, box front and back, 8½" tall, 1956. $75.00.

Face – Wheaties
General Mills, stack of box ends, 1955–1956.

Strato helmet – Pick-A-Pack

General Mills, box front, back, and inserts, 7" tall, 1956. $200.00. Joel Spivak Collection.

Strato helmet

General Mills, assembled cutouts and Nicholas, 8" tall, 1956. $45.00.
Joel Spivak Collection.

Marky Maypo – Maypo

Maltex Company, box front, 7" tall, 1956–1960. $175.00.

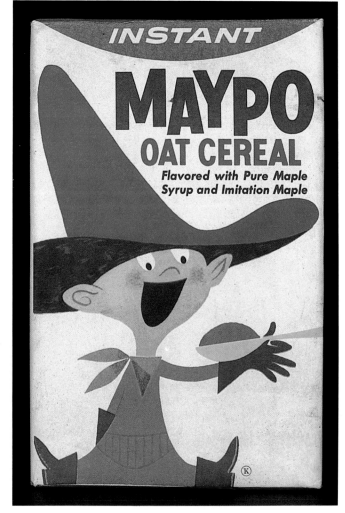

Buffalo Bee hummer and Rin Tin Tin TV mask – Wheat Honeys
Rin Tin Tin barrels of fun – Rice Honeys

National Biscuit, box fronts, 9" tall, 1956. $75.00–100.00 each.

Buffalo Bee hummer toy – Wheat Honeys (left)

National Biscuit, box back, 9" tall, 1956.

Buffalo Bee hummer toy

National Biscuit, assembled cutout, 4" long, 1956. $10.00.

Rin Tin Tin TV mask – Wheat Honeys
National Biscuit, box back, 9" tall, 1956.

Rin Tin Tin, Sgt. O'Hara, and Geronimo masks
National Biscuit, cardboard cutouts, 8½" tall, 1956. $10.00–15.00 each.

Rin Tin Tin Barrels of fun – Rice Honey

National Biscuit, box back, 9" tall, 1956. $75.00–100.00.

Rin Tin Tin barrels of fun
National Biscuit, plastic inpacks, 1" long, 1956. $10.00–15.00 each.

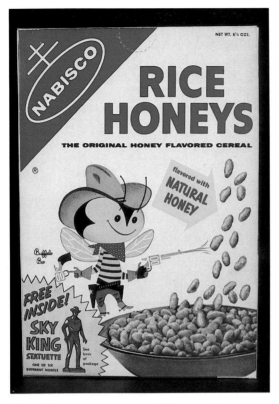

Sky King statuette – Wheat Honeys

National Biscuit Company, box front and back, 9" tall, 1956. $100.00. Mitch Diamond Collection.

Sky King statuettes

National Biscuit Company, plastic figures, 2½" tall, 1956. $10.00–25.00 each. Roland Coover Collection.

Sky King window banner
National Biscuit Company, paper, approx. 24" wide, 1956. $100.00. Don Phelps Collection.

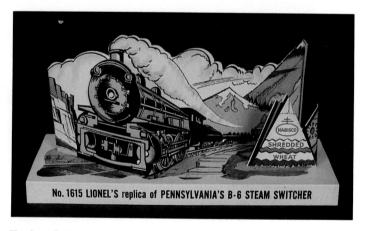

Train-O-Rama
National Biscuit Company, assembled paper diarama, 7" wide, 1956. $25.00–50.00 each. Please Touch Museum Collection.

Train-O-Rama – Shredded Wheat
National Biscuit Company, box back, 6" tall each, 1956. $75.00.

Locomotive hall of fame – Shredded Wheat

National Biscuit Company, box back, 6" tall, 1956. $75.00.

Hall of fame locomotives

National Biscuit Company, assembled paper punchouts, 6" long, 1956. $25.00–35.00 each. Don Simonini Collection.

Army tank, marbles, and circus toy – Toasties

Post/General Foods, box fronts and backs, 11¾" tall, 1956. $50.00–100.00 each.

Army tank
Post/General Foods, plastic with wood balls, 5" long, 1956. $75.00.

Jolly the Circus Horse toy
Post/General Foods, assembled paper punch out, 5" tall, 1956. $10.00–15.00 each.
Roland Coover Collection.

Box backs with additional figures shown below.

**Looney Tunes notch-em toy and circus toy –
Raisin Bran**
Post/General Foods, box fronts and backs, 9½" tall, 1956. $150.00 and $65.00.

Looney Tunes notch-em toys
Post/General Foods, die cut cardboard punch outs, 6" tall, 1956. $15.00–20.00 each. John Fawcett Collection.

Cereal bowls – Post Ten trays

Post/General Foods, tray bottoms, 14" long each, 1956–1957. $25.00.

Cereal bowls

Post/General Foods, plastic, 5½" across, 1956–1957. $15.00–25.00. Roland Coover Collection, Virginia and Ralph Moody Collection.

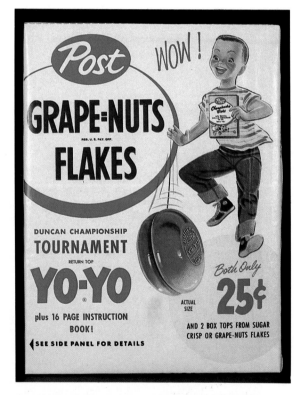

Tourament yo-yo – Grape-Nuts Flakes

Post/General Foods, box back, 9" tall, 1956. $25.00.

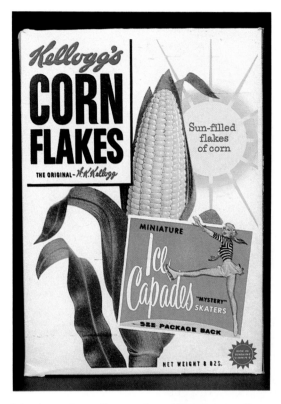 

Mystery Ice Capades skaters – Corn Flakes
Kellogg Company, box front and back, 9½" tall, 1956. $75.00.

Superman satellite launcher
Kellogg Company, plastic (broken sight), 4" long, 1956. $35.00.
Don Simonini Collection.

Superman satellite launcher ad (left)
Kellogg Company, newsprint, 7" wide, 1956. $15.00. Howard Bender Collection.

Flying Superman Corn Flakes mobile
Kellogg Company, diecut cardboard, 35" long, 1956. $1,000.00.

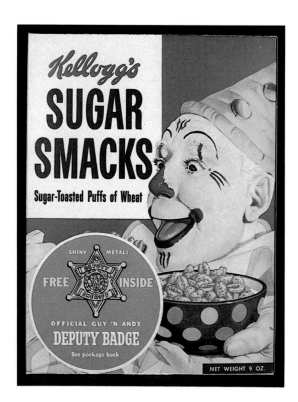

Deputy badge
(Charlie Bell) – Sugar Smacks

Kellogg Company, box front and back, 9½" tall, 1956.
$175.00.

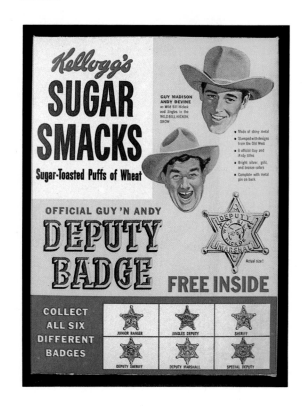

Flying Superman Corn Flakes standee

Kellogg Company, die-cut cardboard, 7' tall [missing jumbo box on top],
1956. $2,500.00–3,500.00. Don Phelps Collection.

Snack Pak
Kellogg Company, loaded tray, 8½" long, 1956. $75.00.

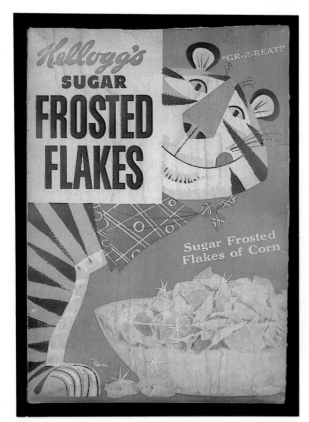

**Tony the Tiger –
Sugar Frosted Flakes**
Kellogg Company, jumbo display box front,
20" tall, 1956. $75.00.

Jingles' American Rifle – Sugar Corn Pops
Kellogg Company, box front and back, 7½" tall, 1956. $175.00.

Jingles – Sugar Corn Pops
Kellogg Company, jumbo display box front, 20" tall, 1956. $150.00.

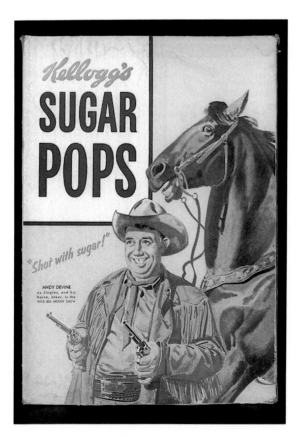

Superman flying rocket (Hickok) – Sugar Corn Pops
Kellogg Company, box front and back, 9½" tall, 1956. $300.00.

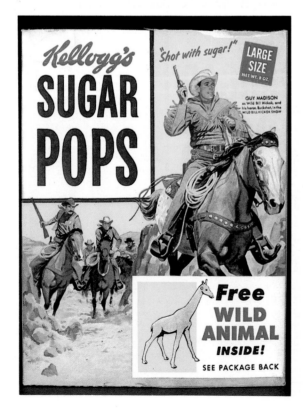

Wild animals Hickok – Sugar Corn Pops
Kellogg Company, box front, 9½" tall, 1956. $125.00.

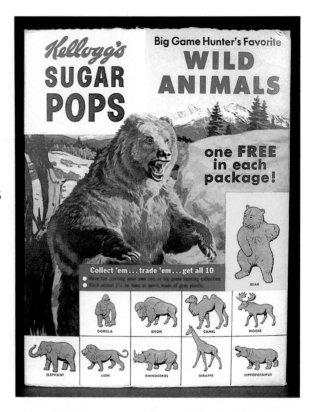

Wild animals Hickok – Sugar Corn Pops

Kellogg Company, box back, 9½" tall, 1956. $125.00.

Wild animals

Kellogg Company, plastic, 1–2½" tall, 1956. $5.00–15.00 each. Roland Coover Collection.

Rice Krispies, Corn Flakes, and Raisin Bran
Kellogg Company, single-serving boxes, 4" tall, 1956. $15.00–25.00 each.

"You're on your own" Variety Pack magazine ad
Kellogg Company, paper, 14" tall, 1956. $5.00.

1957

In 1957...*USSR launches Sputnik into Earth's orbit...Sgt. Preston corners kids to buy Quaker's Ranger Joe knock off, Sugar Puffs...Millions of kids dig through Honeys in search of plastic dinosaurs. "I started the dinosaur craze," claimed their designer, Wally Walworth, years later...Kellogg sponsors "The Woody Woodpecker Show" on TV...Smaxey the Seal slides out on Sugar Smacks...Big G and Warner Bros. get in bed to promote a Lone Ranger movie with supermarket displays and Movie Town cutouts...Post sponsors "Mighty Mouse Playhouse" on TV, adopts Kellogg's square corner card and launches Alpha Bits with the designer's kids' names, Kim and Lyn (sic), spelled out in bowl on cover...Post finds Al Capp a "pain" when series of Li'l Abner cutouts and store signs turn ugly. Artist parts company on a sour note.*

Sgt. Preston Sugar Puffs window sign
Quaker Oats Company, paper, 16" tall, 1957. $75.00.

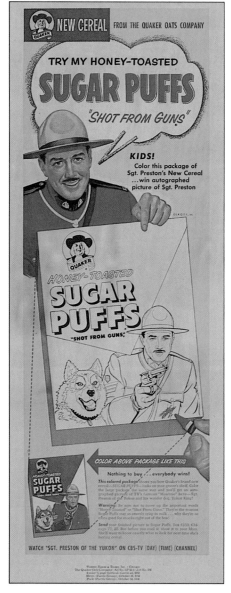

Sgt. Preston Sugar Puffs newspaper ad
Quaker Oats Company, newsprint proof, 21" tall, 1957. $25.00.

Lone Ranger rearing on Silver store display
General Mills, diecut cardboard, 7' tall, 1957. $1,800.00.

Lone Ranger movie town ranch – Cheerios
General Mills, box front and back, 10¼", 1957. $125.00.

Lone Ranger cowboy and Indian figures

General Mills, plastic, 2" tall, 1957. $15.00 each. Dick Fuss Collection.

YOU CAN MAKE YOUR
LONE RANGER MOVIE RANCH
WILD WEST TOWN

LOOK LIKE THIS!

GET ALL 5 BUILDINGS ON
SPECIAL CHEERIOS PACKAGES!
• Frontier Hotel   • Livery Stable
• Sheriff's Office   • Bank
• Express Office

GET ALL THE ADDITIONAL
PLASTIC FIGURE SETS
THAT YOU WISH!

SEE OTHER SIDE

Lone Ranger movie town ranch instruction sheet

General Mills, paper, 11" tall, 1957. $50.00. Photo courtesy of Hake's Americana, York, PA.

Donald Duck's Disneyland adventure – Cheerios
General Mills, box front and back, 8½" tall, 1957. $100.00.

Lone Ranger lassoing Cheerios pole display
General Mills, diecut cardboard (missing stack of Cheerios cases), 7' tall, 1957. $2,500.00. Don Phelps Collection.

Lone Ranger hike-o-meter – Wheaties
General Mills, box front and back, 10¼" tall, 1957. $300.00.

Lone Ranger hike-o-meter
General Mills, metal, 2½" across, 1957. $50.00.

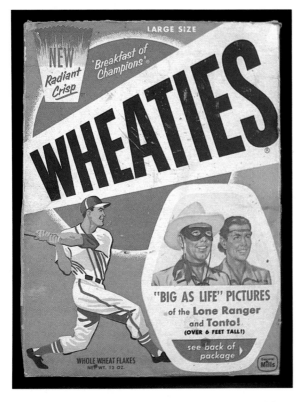

Lone Ranger "big as life" poster – Wheaties

General Mills, box front and back, 10¼" tall, 1957. $300.00.

Lone Ranger "big as life" posters

General Mills, paper, 6' tall, 1957. $100.00 each. John Fawcett Collection.

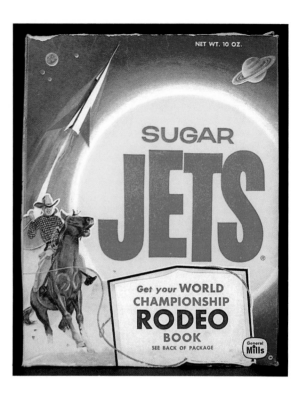

Championship rodeo book – Jets
General Mills, box front and back, 8½" tall, 1957. $100.00.

Lone Ranger standee
General Mills, diecut cardboard, 6' tall, 1957. $1,500.00. John Fawcett Collection.

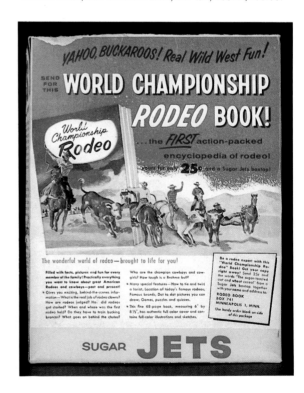

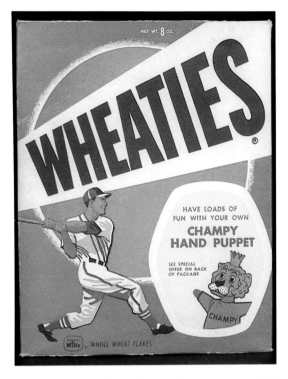

Champy the Lion hand puppet – Wheaties

General Mills, box front and back, 8½" tall, 1957. $125.00.

Champy and Mr. Fox hand puppets

General Mills, vinyl and cloth, 7½" tall, 1957. $25.00–50.00. Phil Arthurhultz Collection.

Roy Rogers jigsaw puzzle and Dick Tracy decoder – Sugar Crisp
Post/General Foods, box fronts and backs, 9½" tall, 1957. $150.00 each.

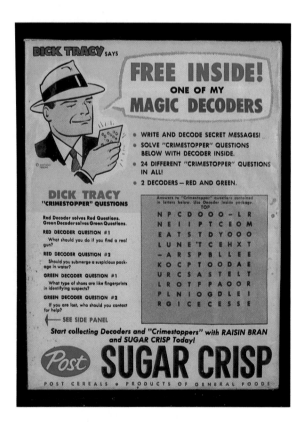

Dick Tracy decoders
Post/General Foods, paper, 3½" across, 1957. $15.00 each. Roland Coover and Nelson Corey Collections.

Alpha Bits
Post/General Foods, box front, 9½" tall, 1957. $100.00.

Captain Jolly – Sugar Corn Fetti
Post/General Foods, box front, 9½" tall, 1957. $100.00.

Circus tent – Sugar Rice Krinkles

Post/General Foods, box front and back, 9" tall, 1957. $75.00.

Two Toasties magazine ads

Post/General Foods, paper, 14" tall, 1957. $6.00 each.

Bowl and mug set, and
Mighty Mouse t-shirt and cape – Toasties
Post/General Foods, box fronts and backs, 11½" and 9½" tall, 1957. $100.00 and $300.00.

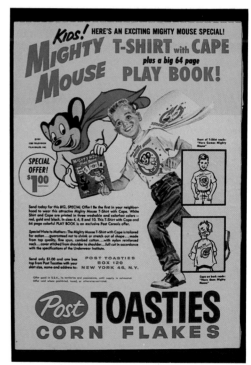

Clown and bear bowls, and clown pitcher
Post/General Foods, plastic, 5½" across, 1957. $10.00–20.00 each. Roland Coover Collection.

Mighty Mouse mystery pictures – Sugar Crisp
Post/General Foods, box front and back, 10½" tall, 1957. $100.00.

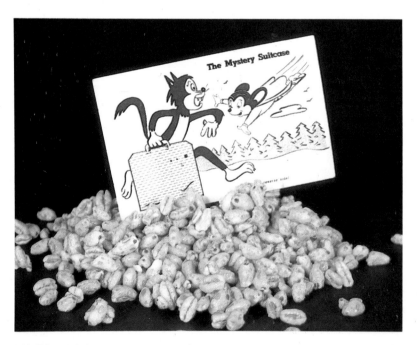

Mighty Mouse mystery picture
Post/General Foods, paper, 5½" across, 1957. $25.00–35.00. Steve Roden Collection.

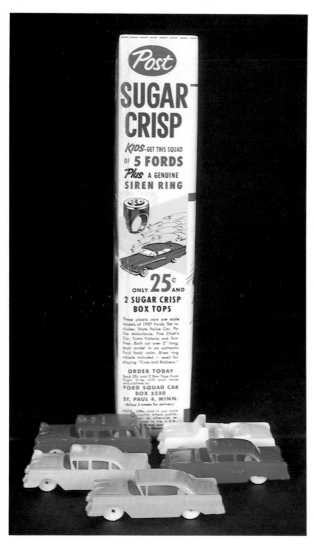

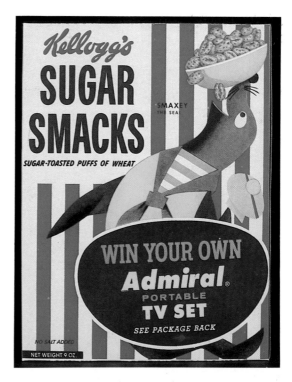

**Admiral TV (Smaxey the Seal) –
Sugar Smacks**
Kellogg Company, box front, 10" tall, 1957. $150.00.

Five Ford squad cars
Post/General Foods, Sugar Crisp box side panel, plastic models,
3" long, 1957. $40.00 each. Larry Blodget Collection.

**Smaxey the Seal
fan club pinback**
Kellogg Company, metal,
1" across, probably 1957.
$10.00.

Smaxey the Seal – Sugar Smacks
Kellogg Company, single serving box, 4" tall, 1957.
$75.00.

Kid quarterback and catcher – Pep
Kellogg Company of Canada, box fronts, 10¼" tall, 1957. $50.00 each.

Admiral TV – Sugar Frosted Flakes
Kellogg Company, box front, 9½" tall, 1957. $100.00.

Mister Twister and Woody Woodpecker crispy treats – Rice Krispies
Kellogg Company, box fronts, 8" and 10¼" tall, 1956–1957. $45.00 and $125.00.

Woody Woodpecker crispy treats Rice Krispies magazine ad
Kellogg Company, paper, 14" tall, 1957. $7.00.

U.S. Navy warships – Raisin Bran

Kellogg Company, box front and back, 8" tall, 1957. $125.00.

Printing set (Jingles) – Sugar Pops

Kellogg Company, box front, 9½" tall, 1957. $150.00.

Jingles – Sugar Pops

Kellogg Company, single serving box, 4" tall, 1957. $75.00.

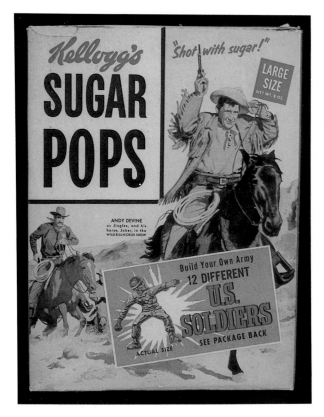

U.S. soldiers (Jingles) – Sugar Pops
Kellogg Company, box front and back, 9½" tall, 1957. $125.00.

U.S. soldiers
Kellogg Company, plastic, 1½" to 2¼" tall, 1957. $3.00–5.00 each.

Dinosaurs – Wheat Honeys
Prehistoric Beasts – Rice Honeys

National Biscuit Company, box fronts and backs, 9" tall, 1957. $100.00 each.

Dinosaurs
National Biscuit Company, plastic figures, 2" long, 1957. $15.00–20.00 each. Roland Coover Collection.

Prehistoric Beasts
National Biscuit Company, plastic figures, 2" long, 1957. $15.00–20.00 each. Roland Coover Collection.

Li'l Abner picture – Toasties
Li'l Abner's contest – 40% Bran Flakes

Post/General Foods, box fronts, 12" and 9½" tall, 1957. $75.00 and $100.00.

Li'l Abner's contest – Grape Nuts Flakes
Li'l Abner picture – Raisin Bran

Post/General Foods, box fronts, 12" and 9½" tall, 1957–1958. $100.00 each.

Li'l Abner's contest display

Post/General Foods, diecut cardboard, 65" tall, 1957–1958. $350.00.

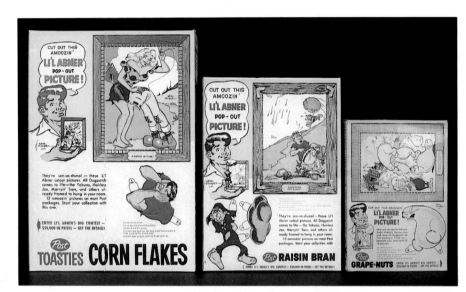

Li'l Abner pictures
Post/General Foods, various box backs, 1957.

Li'l Abner cutouts (below)
Post/General Foods, assemblied cutouts, 5–6" tall, 1957. $10.00–20.00 each.

In 1958...Pan Am inaugurates jet passenger service between US and Britain...Kellogg rolls out new "bank note" design of little Kellogg's signatures against a white background... Jose the Monkey says Cocoa Krispies is "Like a chocolate milkshake, only crunchy"...Post trashes the wax-over wrap and picks up Kellogg's orphaned brand colors...Animated corn cob named Cornelius C. Sugarcoat turns Corn Fetti into Sugar Coated Corn Flakes...Plastic spoonmen named Crunchy, Munchy, and Spoonsize become space age Snap, Crackle, and Pop...Quaker turns Sugar Puffs over to Mort Moose and Wally Walrus before snuffing brand...Olympic gold medal winner Bob Richards champions Wheaties and becomes the first athlete on the front of a cereal box. "It was an honor," Richards said years later.

Mr. Moonbird's toy certificate – Jets
General Mills, box front and back, 8½" tall, 1958. $100.00.

Airport hanger – Cheerios
General Mills, box front and back, 9½" tall, 1958. $65.00.

Airport instruction sheet – Cheerios
General Mills, paper, 11" tall, 1958. $50.00.

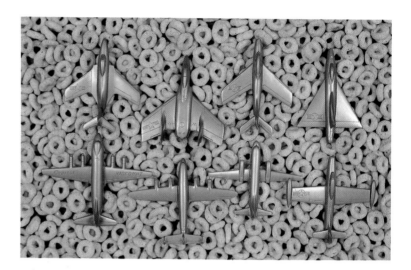

Airport airplanes – Cheerios
General Mills, plastic, 2½–3" long, 1958. $5.00–15.00 each.

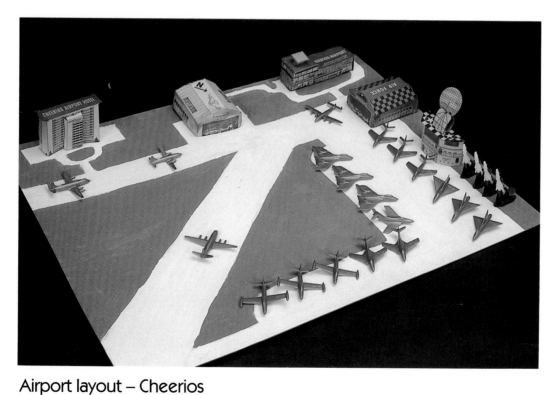

Airport layout – Cheerios
General Mills, cutouts, plastic planes and missiles on homemade base, approx. 30" long, 1958. $125.00.

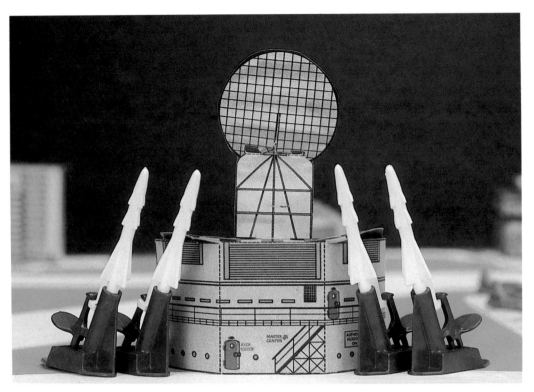

Airport missile station (closeup)

Airport terminal (closeup)

Right: Airport hotel and crashing jet (closeup)

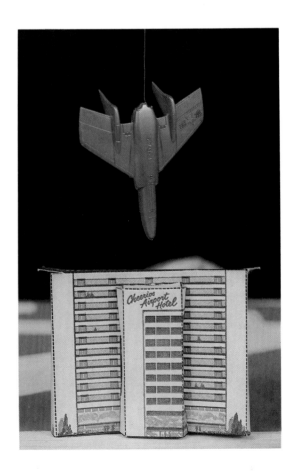

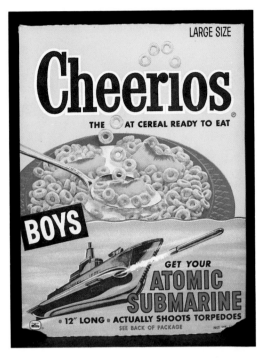

Atomic submarine – Cheerios
General Mills, box front and back, 9½" tall, 1958. $50.00.

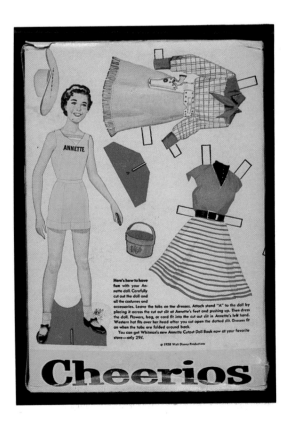

Annette doll – Cheerios
General Mills, box front and back, 9½" tall, 1958. $300.00.

Annette doll
General Mills, assembled cutouts, 7" tall, 1958. $15.00.

Bob Richards' fitness tester – Wheaties
General Mills, box front and back, 10¼" tall, 1958. $100.00.

Bob Richards' fitness tester
General Mills, cardboard cutout and scotch tape, 12" long, 1958. $10.00.

Wyatt Earp marshal's ring
General Mills, sterling silver, 1" across, 1958. $100.00–150.00.
Bob Hummrich Collection.

Wyatt Earp marshal's ring – Cheerios
General Mills, box front and back, 8½" tall, 1958. $125.00.

Rin Tin Tin – Shredded Wheat Juniors
Rin Tin Tin insignia badge and Rin Tin Tin TV scene – Shredded Wheat
National Biscuit Company, box fronts and backs, 8" and 6" tall, 1958. $100.00 each.

Rin Tin Tin insignia badges
National Biscuit Company, sticky paper, 2½" square, 1958. $10.00–15.00 each.
Ed Pragler Collection.

Mort and Wally Sugar Puffs newspaper ad

Quaker Oats Company, newsprint proof, 21" long, 1958. $25.00.

Sugar Coated Corn Flakes magazine ad

Post/General Foods, paper, 14" tall, 1958. $5.00.

"Men of action" Alpha Bits magazine ad

Post/General Foods, paper, 14" tall, 1958. $5.00.

Mighty Mouse blow pipe – Sugar Coated Corn Flakes
Mighty Mouse merry pack – Alpha Bits
Post/General Foods, box fronts and backs, 9½" tall, 1958. $125.00 each.

"Eatingest youngsters eat . . ." Sugar Crisp magazine ad
Post/General Foods, paper, 14" tall, 1958. $5.00.

B-58 bomber, Mighty Mouse TV mask, and TV game – Sugar Crisp

Post/General Foods, box fronts and backs, 10½" and 9½" tall, 1958. $65.00, $100.00, and $125.00.

Mighty Mouse TV masks
Post/General Foods, cutouts, 10" tall, 1958. $15.00–25.00 each.

B-58 bomber model
Post/General Foods, assembled plastic, 12½" long, 1958. $75.00.

Sugar Crisp box back shown at left.

SAC survival rifle – Toasties
Post/General Foods, box back, 11¾" tall, 1958. $100.00.

Woody Woodpecker contest and U.S. Army flying platform – Corn Flakes
Kellogg Company, box fronts, 9½" tall, 1957–1958. $125.00 and $45.00.

Woody Woodpecker contest and U.S. Army flying platform – Corn Flakes
Kellogg Company, box backs, 9½" tall, 1957–1958.

U.S. Army flying platform
Kellogg Company, plastic, 6" wide, 1957–1958. $35.00.

Battery-powered electric train – Corn Flakes

Kellogg Company, box front and back, 9¾" tall, 1957–1958. $100.00.

Battery-powered electric train set

Kellogg Company, cardboard punch outs and plastic. Locomotive: 7¾" long, 1957–1958. $75.00. Don Simonini Collection.

Armored knights and jet clipper – Corn Flakes
Kellogg Company, box fronts and backs, 11½" and 9½" tall, 1957–1958. $75.00 and $50.00.

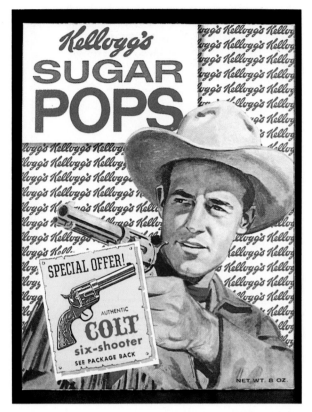

Colt six-shooter (Hickok) – Sugar Pops

Kellogg Company, box front and back, 9½" tall, 1958. $225.00.

Hickok Colt six-shooter

Kellogg Company, plastic, 10" long, 1958. $150.00. Steve Roden Collection.

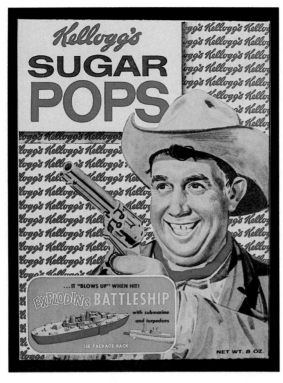

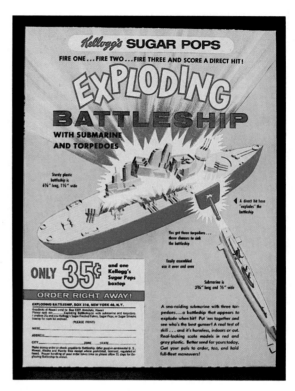

Exploding battleship (Jingles) – Sugar Pops
Kellogg Company, box front and back, 9½" tall, 1958. $225.00.

Sweet Eatin' stampede motorized display
Kellogg Company, cardboard and electric motor (behind), 39" tall, 1958. $750.00. Photo by Peter A. Smith.

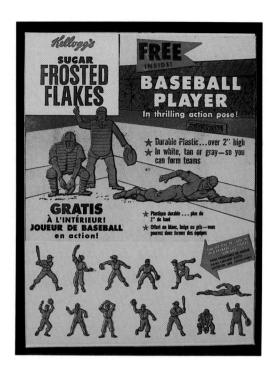

Colt six-shooter and baseball player – Sugar Frosted Flakes

Kellogg Company (U.S. and Canada), box fronts, 9½" and 9" tall, 1958. $125.00 and $65.00.

Baseball players

Kellogg Company of Canada, plastic, 1½–2½" tall, 1958. $10.00–15.00 each. Virginia and Ralph Moody Collection.

"Variety settles differences"
Variety Pack magazine ad
Kellogg Company, paper, 14" tall, 1958. $5.00.

"The serious side"
Rice Krispies magazine ad
Kellogg Company, paper, 14" tall, 1958. $5.00.

Topsy-turvy top – Sugar Smacks
Kellogg Company of Canada, box front, 10" tall, 1958.
$100.00.

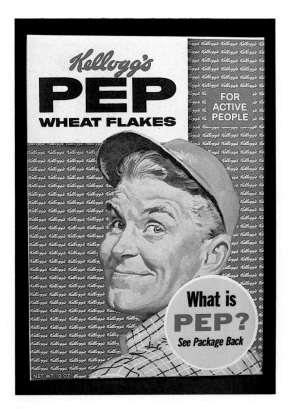

Pep
Kellogg Company, box front, 9½" tall, 1958. $55.00.

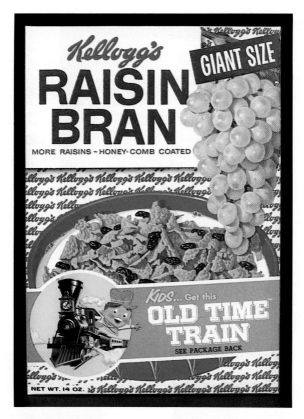

Old time train toy – Raisin Bran
Kellogg Company, box front, 10" tall, 1958. $125.00.

Old time train toy
Kellogg Company, plastic train and box back. Train: 13" long, 1958. $15.00. Don Simonini Collection.

**Woody kazoo and
Woody Woodpecker club cap –
Rice Krispies**

Kellogg Company, box fronts and backs, 8½" tall,
1958. $125.00 each.

Woody Woodpecker kazoo
(below)

Kellogg Company, plastic, 6½" tall, 1958. $35.00.

Woody Woodpecker club cap
Kellogg Company, cloth with plastic crest, 11½" long, 1958. $45.00.

Jose the Monkey newspaper ad
Kellogg Company, newsprint proof, 17" tall, 1958. $25.00.

Jose the Monkey – Cocoa Krispies
Kellogg Company, box front, 9½" tall, 1958. $145.00.

1959

In 1959...Alaska becomes the 49th state...Big G looses Frosty the Supercharged Bear to push its sugar-coated Cheerios...Three toddlers known as the Cocoa Puff Kids make a tenuous connection between the chocolate balls and trains...Kellogg sponsors "The Huckleberry Hound Show" after Post turns it down...Prairie dog named Sugar Pops Pete "sweetens up" local riff-raff with his candy-striped "Sugar Popper"...Marlboro Man creator cooks up Big Otis for Kellogg's OKs...Yogi Bear tags the kilted warrior "Big Oafish"...Tie-ins to Post sponsored "Danny Thomas Show" sing and dance on Toasties...After years of dreaming about it, a Post artist kills off two of the three Sugar Crisp bears. "They were gone," cries the joyous artist. "I couldn't believe it!...In the end, it was so easy!"

Spoonman – Shredded Wheat Juniors

National Biscuit Company, box front and back, 7¾" tall, 1959. $150.00. Please Touch Museum Collection.

Crunchy, Munchy, and Spoonsize Spoonmen

National Biscuit Company, plastic, 2" tall, 1959. $15.00–25.00. Roland Coover Collection.

Aircraft carrier and Tobor the robot – Shredded Wheat Juniors

National Biscuit Company, box fronts and backs, 7¾" tall, 1959. $45.00 and $100.00.

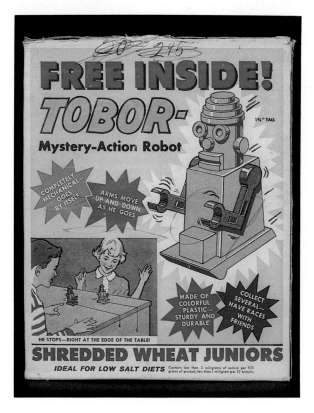

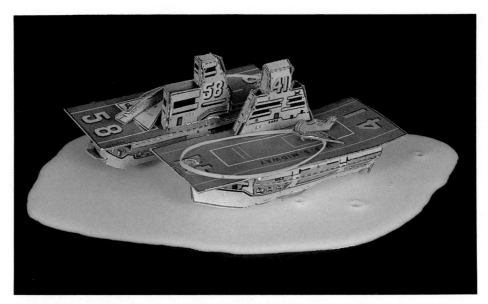

Aircraft carriers
National Biscuit Company, assembled cutouts, 4½" long, 1959. $10.00–15.00 each.

Tobor the robot
National Biscuit Company, plastic, 1¾" tall, 1959. $50.00.

Buffalo Bee comic book
National Biscuit Company, newsprint, 10¼" tall, 1959. $25.00.
Howard Bender Collection.

Thunderbird model – Sugar Rice Krinkles
Post/General Foods, box front and back, 9½" tall, 1959. $100.00.

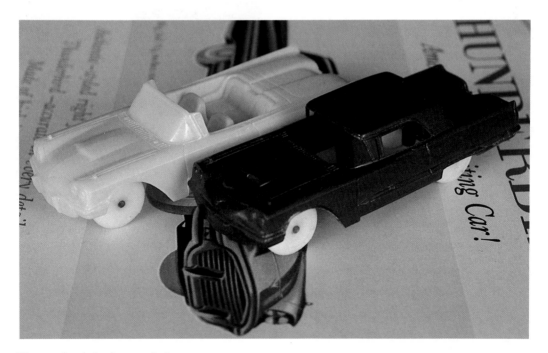

Thunderbird model cars
Post/General Foods, plastic, 3" long, 1959. $15.00–25.00 each.

Walking Cornelius toy –
Sugar Coated Corn Flakes

Post/General Foods, box front and back, 11" tall, 1959.
$150.00.

Cornelius C. Sugarcoat walking toy

Post/General Foods, plastic, 6¼" tall, 1959. $150.00–200.00.
Phil Arthurhultz Collection.

Sugar Coated Corn Flakes and Toasties

Post/General Foods, single serving boxes, 4" tall, 1959. $35.00 and $15.00.

Danny Thomas album and spin-a-part Danny Thomas game – Toasties

Post/General Foods, box fronts and back, 9½" and 11½" tall, 1959. $150.00 each.

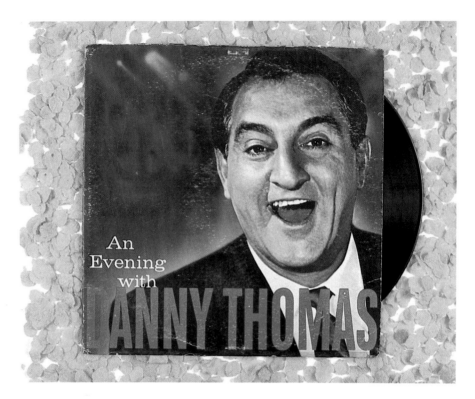

"An Evening with Danny Thomas" album
Post/General Foods, record cover front and back, 12½" wide, 1959. $50.00. Roland Coover Collection.

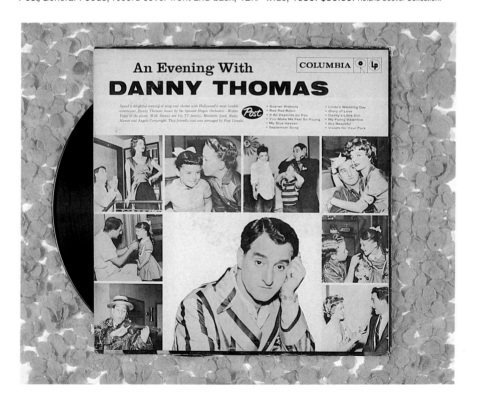

Spin-a-part Danny Thomas game

Post/General Foods, box back and scattered cutouts, 1959. $15.00–20.00.

Linda Williams doll – Toasties

Post/General Foods, box back, 9½" tall, 1959. $85.00.

Sweepstakes – Grape Nuts Flakes
Fury bronco buster game – Raisin Bran
Post/General Foods, box fronts and back, 12" and 8½" tall, 1959. $25.00 and $100.00.

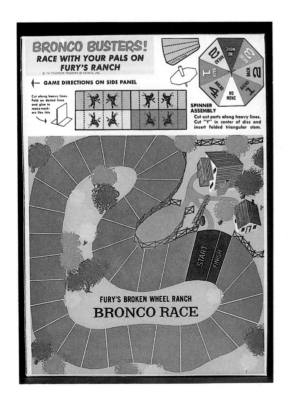

Fury bronco buster game
Post/General Foods, assembled cutouts, 6" across, 1959. $10.00–20.00.

Sweet Eatin' round-up! window banner
Kellogg Company, paper, 39" long, 1959. $250.00.

Movie outfit – Sugar Frosted Flakes
Kellogg Company, box front, 9½" tall, 1959. $75.00.

Smaxey the Seal action cutout –
Sugar Smacks
Kellogg Company, box front, 10" tall, 1959. $100.00.

Sugar Pops Pete action cutout – Sugar Pops
Kellogg Company, box front and back, 9½" tall, 1959. $100.00.

Sugar Pops Pete and Smaxey action toys
Kellogg Company, assembled cutouts, 5" tall, 1959. $10.00.

Cocoa Krispies, Sugar Smacks, and Sugar Pops

Kellogg Company, single serving boxes, 4" tall, 1959. $45.00 each.

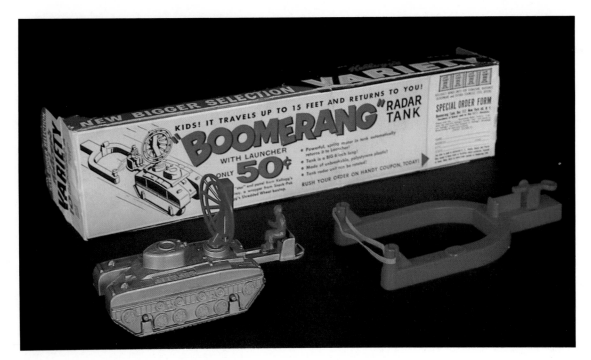

Variety tray and boomerang radar tank with launcher

Kellogg Company, tray bottom and plastic toy. Tank: 6" long, 1959. $15.00 and $25.00.

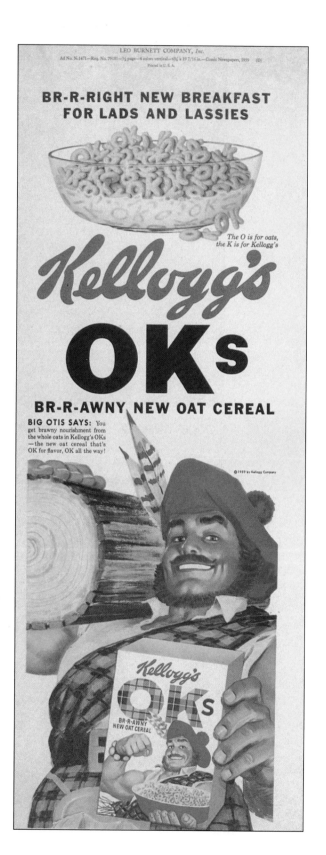

OKs newspaper ads
Kellogg Company, newsprint proofs, 21" tall, 1959. $35.00 (above) and $15.00 (right).

Catapult game (Big Otis) – OKs
Kellogg Company, box front, 11¼" tall, 1959–1960. $100.00.

Turbo beam car – Rice Krispies
Kellogg Company, box front and back, 11¼" tall, 1959. $75.00.

Huckleberry Hound fun cards and toy statues — Corn Flakes
Kellogg Company, box fronts and backs, 11½" and 12½" tall, 1959. $150.00 each.

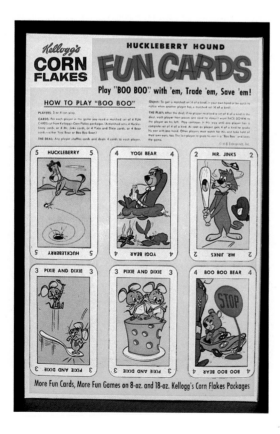

Huckleberry Hound fun cards
Kellogg Company, cutouts, 3½" long, 1959. $5.00–10.00 each.

Huckleberry Hound toy statues
Kellogg Company, plastic, 1½" to 2" tall, 1959. $15.00–25.00 each. Roland Coover Collection.

40% Bran Flakes and 1959 Chevrolet Impala – Corn Flakes

Kellogg Company, box fronts and back, 10¼" and 9½" tall, 1959. $25.00 and $75.00.

Pontiac sweepstakes – Trix, Wheaties, and Jets
General Mills, box fronts and back, 8½–13" tall, 1958–1959. $100.00–150.00 each.

Pontiac Bonneville car
General Mills, plastic and metal, 8½" long, 1958–1959. $125.00.

Conductor's cut outs – Cocoa Puffs

General Mills, box front and back, 8½" tall, 1959. $45.00.

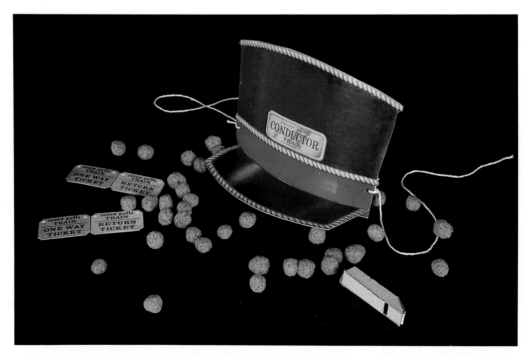

Conductor's hat, tickets, and whistle

General Mills, assembled cutouts. Hat: 4¼" tall, 1959. $5.00–15.00 each.

Win Lionel layout – Cocoa Puffs

General Mills, box front and back, 8½" tall, 1959. $75.00.

Cartoon theater – Cocoa Puffs

General Mills, box front and back, 8½" tall, 1959. $65.00.

Cartoon theater
General Mills, assembled cutouts, 8½" tall, 1959. $15.00–35.00.

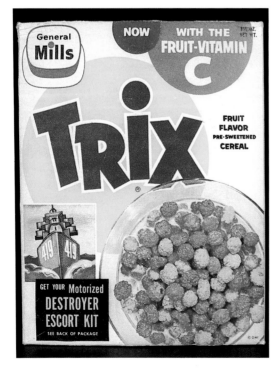

Motorized destroyer escort – Trix
General Mills, box front and back, 9½" tall, 1959. $65.00.

Frosty O's
General Mills, box front, 8¼" tall, 1959. $125.00.

Frosty Bear display
General Mills, two-sided cardboard, 39" tall, 1959. $325.00.

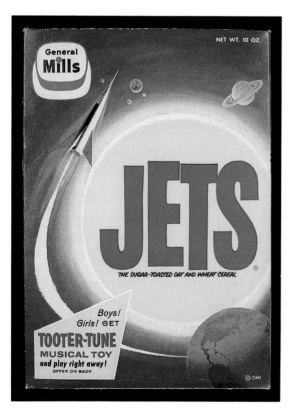

Tooter tune – Jets
General Mills, box front, 9½" tall, 1959–1960. $150.00.

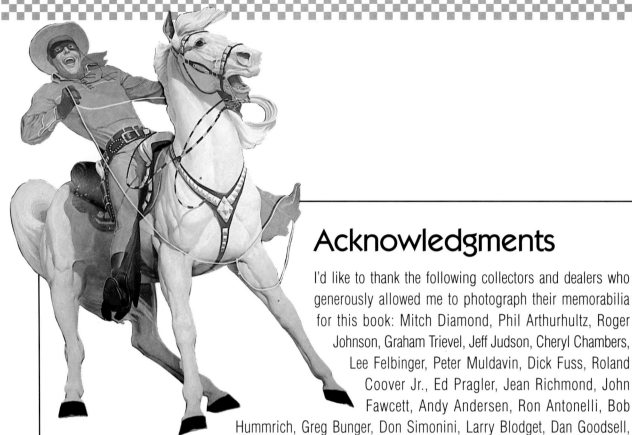

Acknowledgments

I'd like to thank the following collectors and dealers who generously allowed me to photograph their memorabilia for this book: Mitch Diamond, Phil Arthurhultz, Roger Johnson, Graham Trievel, Jeff Judson, Cheryl Chambers, Lee Felbinger, Peter Muldavin, Dick Fuss, Roland Coover Jr., Ed Pragler, Jean Richmond, John Fawcett, Andy Andersen, Ron Antonelli, Bob Hummrich, Greg Bunger, Don Simonini, Larry Blodget, Dan Goodsell, Steve Roden, Lou Antonicello, Betty Ann Bunger, Danny Fuchs, David Gutterman, Howard Bender, Larry Fenske, Elliott H. Berger, Dan Woods, Nelson Corey, Virginia and Ralph Moody, Bruce Cervon, Gary Hunter, Don Phelps, Joel Spivak, Jim Cole, and Kristin Peszka at the Please Touch Museum for Children in Philadelphia. Rick Hirsh loaned slides. Ted Hake did too, though with the proviso that I print "word for word" and in type "larger than 5 point," the following advertisement. "Hake's Americana & Collectibles has specialized in character collectibles and nostalgia memorabilia since 1967. To receive a catalogue for their next mail-and-phone bid auction offering 3,000 popular culture collectibles, send $6.00 to Hake's Americana, P.O. Box 1444M, York, PA 17405." *Whew!*

Special thanks to photographer Peter A. Smith, who taught me how to take the pictures in this book and loaned me cameras and lenses on occasions beyond count. Peter V. Scott helped me lug photo equipment around Greater Paramus. Diane Albert, Dale Ames, Ralph MacPhail, Bob Traverse, Bill Betts, Heidi LaFleche, and Joan and Jack Wareing were also of great help. Prototypes of the field-of-cereal chapter openers were designed by Bruce Crocker. Finally, a million thanks to my editor Lisa Stroup and designer Karen Geary at Collector Books for making this project not only painless, but often a lot of fun.

All correspondence regarding this book or *Flake* magazine should be directed to:

Scott Bruce
PO Box 481, Dept. KY,
Cambridge, MA 02140
(617) 492-5004

About the Author/Photographer

Scott Bruce, known as Mr. Cereal Box, is the publisher of *Flake* magazine and has appeared on *Today, CNN, CBS Morning News, Entertainment Tonight,* and many other TV shows talking about cereal. His other books include *Cerealizing America: The Unsweetened Story of American Breakfast Cereal* (with Bill Crawford), *Lunch Box: The Fifties and Sixties,* and *The Official Price Guide to Lunch Box Collectibles.* He lives in Cambridge, Massachusetts.

The Definitive History Is Here!

- Intro by Chuck McCann
- More than 300 pages
- Black & white photos
- 40 hilarious sidebars
- Spellbinding writing
- Hardcover

$24.95

"*Cerealizing America* really tells it like it was. From now on, it's Kellogg's from Up-the-Creek!" — Max Baer, Jethro on *The Beverly Hillbillies.*

Cerealizing America: The Unsweetened Story of American Breakfast Cereal by Scott Bruce and Bill Crawford is here. Part expose, part celebration, this book strips the sugar coating from the history of breakfast culture to reveal the origin and evolution of America's obsession with health, hucksterism and toy surprises. You'll laugh out loud at revelations about Dr. Kellogg, C.W. Post, Babe Ruth, Walt Disney, Superman, the Lone Ranger, Tony the Tiger, Jay Ward, Roy Rogers, Marky Maypo, Twinkles, Quisp and Quake, Trix Rabbit, Hanna-Barbera, Beverly Hillbillies, Linus the Lionhearted, Andy Griffith, Jim Nabors, Monkees, Michael Jackson, Banana Splits, King Vitaman, Freakies, and other breakfast heroes.

"I'm cuckoo for this book. Wuuuuwwk!" **Chuck McCann,** actor/writer and voice of the original cuckoo bird.

"Gosh, the boys did their homework. *Cerealizing America* is GR-R-REAT!" **Thurl Ravenscroft,** voice of Tony the Tiger.

"The childhood memories I cherish most are those of breakfast spent engrossed in the storybook back of a Twinkles box or fascinated by the artwork of Jay Ward's Quisp, Quake, Cap'n Crunch or Quangaroos... [Cerealizing America] captured those moments beautifully." **Mark Hamill,** Star Wars' Luke Skywalker.

To order your copy of *Cerealizing America,* call

1-800-666-2211

For more information, please contact Faber and Faber publishers at 617-721-1427